Crisis and Opportunity

Devon Foot and Mouth Inquiry 2001

Final Report

Inquiry Chairman:
Professor Ian Mercer CBE

DEVON
BOOKS

First published in Great Britain in 2002

This report is being made available on Devon County Council's website,
www.devon.gov.uk
Large format versions are available on request from Devon County Council's
Local Government Information Centre and Library on 01392 383444
or info@devon.gov.uk

British Library Cataloguing-in-Publication Data

A CIP record for this title is available from the British Library.

ISBN 1-85522-822-X

DEVON BOOKS
Official Publisher to Devon County Council
Halsgrove House
Lower Moor Way
Tiverton Devon EX16 6SS

Tel 01884 243242
Fax 01884 243325

email sales@halsgrove.com
website www.halsgrove.com

Front cover photograph: County Gate, looking down the East Lyn Valley
towards Brendon (Ernest Davey)
Back cover photograph: The Devon Foot and Mouth Inquiry in session
October 2001 (Apex)
Designed and typeset by Devon Design and Print, Exeter
Printed and bound in Great Britain by Kingfisher Print, Totnes

Contents

Foot and Mouth Disease in Devon 2001

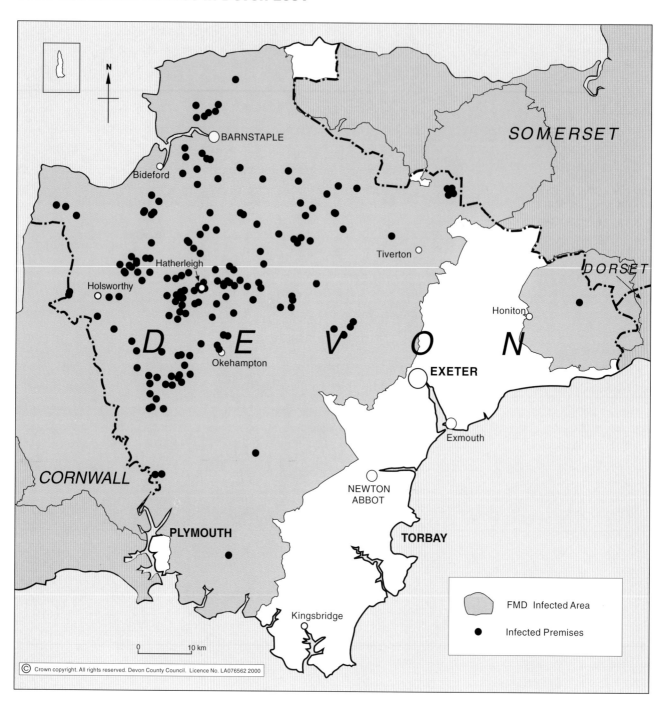

SOMERSET

BARNSTAPLE

Bideford

DORSET

Tiverton

Hatherleigh

Holsworthy

Honiton

D E V O N

Okehampton

EXETER

Exmouth

CORNWALL

NEWTON
ABBOT

PLYMOUTH

TORBAY

Kingsbridge

0   10 km

FMD Infected Area

Infected Premises

© Crown copyright. All rights reserved. Devon County Council. Licence No. LA076562 2000

Preface

The preliminary findings of the Devon Inquiry into the Foot and Mouth epidemic of 2001 and its consequences were published on 29 October of that year. Between these covers is the final version of those findings modified only in the interests of greater clarity and because of events or information received since October.

The findings are supported now by an edited selection from some 380 submissions made to the Inquiry (all of which will in due course be held in the Devon Record Office), and by Chris Chapman's powerful photographs taken on one farm in north Devon, beginning before the effect of the epidemic struck and continuing until the bitter end.

It is intended that this triptych will illustrate more clearly for those remote in space or time from the events in Devon, the lamentable circumstances which over half the County suffered in 2001.

The Devon Inquiry Committee in session, County Hall, Exeter in October 2001

The Report

Into the outbreak and its effects, their handling now and in the future and the recovery and sustaining of the well-being of Devon's countryside.

Foreword

Following the Foot and Mouth crisis that began in February 2001 which had such a devastating effect on the economy of the County of Devon and indeed the whole country, the County Council decided to organise an Inquiry in public into the outbreak. A Committee (Appendix 1) was set up of County and District Councillors under an independent Chairman (Professor Ian Mercer) to oversee the conduct of the Inquiry. Terms of Reference (Appendix 2) were adopted to guide the Inquiry Committee and anyone submitting evidence. The Inquiry's findings were to be forwarded to the three separate Government Inquiries (set up after the Devon decision); to support the County Council's bid for funding under the Devon Recovery Plan and to give an opportunity to the people of Devon who wanted to express their distress as well as their hopes for the future.

The Inquiry was widely publicised in the media and individuals and organisations were encouraged and assisted to make submissions either via the Internet or by letter. In the final analysis some 380 submissions were made to the Inquiry, with over 80 via the Internet. Of those submissions 28% were from farmers, 38% were from interested bodies and organisations and 34% were from businesses and individual members of the public.

Sitting in public, its proceedings continuously available on the Internet, the Committee questioned a balanced range of selected witnesses. Government NDPBs (Non Departmental Public Bodies) - English Nature, Environment, Countryside and Regional Development Agencies - were joined by Dartmoor and Exmoor National Park Authorities and powerful Non-Government Organisations - National Farmers' Union (NFU), Royal Society for the Prevention of Cruelty to Animals (RSPCA), National Trust and Royal Society for the Protection of Birds (RSPB). The Devon and Cornwall Constabulary, North and East Devon Health Authority, the County Council and the District Councils most affected also appeared. Devon Federations of Young Farmers' Clubs and Women's Institutes, Associations of Parish Councils and Veterinarians shared witness with individual parish clerks and chairmen, and vets. An Anglican priest, a Citizens' Advice Bureau officer, the Farm Crisis Network and a primary school headmaster and governor gave the

Committee an insight into the psychological scenario in which they found themselves earlier this year. They extended the individual accounts of farmers and their families who were directly affected, those who were not and non-farming families. Tourist industry representatives and senior figures from each branch of the local media ensured that the whole spectrum of those involved in the outbreak and its aftermath had their chance to expand upon what they had written.

That the Department of Environment Food and Rural Affairs (DEFRA) declined the invitation to attend the hearings has been deplored by many. Ministers had in the end agreed to provide written answers to questions sent by the County Council (Appendix 6), and to supplementary questions which might then arise. The relevant documents are set out in Appendices 7 and 8 with the dates of their arrival in Devon. It seems fairer to DEFRA to print the 20th December response in its entirety in one place than to insert notes culled from it and relevant retorts at points throughout our own text (except in the case of Form D farmers). We welcome the effort made to provide 'Comments to Inquiries' produced in part we assume because of the Devon initiative and the receipt of our preliminary findings by DEFRA on 29th October. It is difficult in matters such as this to separate reality at the time (up to nine months ago) from retrospective thinking, but in either case our concern for the poverty of communication during the early weeks of the outbreak is confirmed by what we now read. Many statements in the DEFRA response invite further questions because they are vague, open ended or inaccurate (where we have been able to check them). We expect that a dialogue between the County Council and DEFRA will continue on these matters. There is otherwise little in the response that causes us to modify the findings we have made from the many submissions made to us.

The matter of contingency planning however does merit attention here and qualification in our chapter 2. DEFRA, having confirmed that MAFF did have a contingency plan, concedes that it was 'largely internal' and that the 'unprecedented' scale of the outbreak 'exceeded the ability of the resources available......to deal with it effectively'. We welcome the reference to a revised contingency plan which will be more inclusive, include local stakeholders and be informed by the 'Lessons Learned' inquiry. We trust that it will be informed by all Inquiries' results, and we feel that our preliminary findings in this respect are wholly vindicated and need only slight refinement now.

It is a nice judgement in retrospect whether cross-examination of Ministers not in office at the time, or of locally based civil servants who might claim they were not responsible for decisions made centrally, all in inevitably defensive mode, would have enhanced the public proceedings in Devon. Timing, and the time to be taken, could have meant that such an exercise was frustrating and unproductive, not least to those whose evidence might have been squeezed out. As many have claimed, a thorough national and formal public inquiry (able to summon ex-Ministers and civil servants at all levels) would be a more appropriate process for holding central Government players to account. But, even then, the fencing of legal advocates and defenders could prolong, perplex and confuse the issues until the truth was even more deeply buried than it is now. It is after all, already quite clear that the outbreak and the handling of the ensuing crisis was lamentable.

Preliminary findings and recommendations were produced in 14 days so that they could be forwarded to the Government's Policy Commission on the Future of Farming and Food whose chairman, Sir Don Curry, had asked for responses to his consultation by the 26th October. They were inevitably in an unpolished form given the time constraint (this Inquiry sat until the 12th October). In the end that set of Preliminary Findings, its timely appearance and economic format, were widely welcomed. It promised a final and definitive report and hence this document, which attempts to retain the same virtues.

Nevertheless in the short time we had to produce the original, some evidence was given less justice than it deserved, some things were omitted by chance and of course things have happened since we sat - not least the lifting of restrictions in Devon in December. One of the things we recommended - the mounting of an international dialogue about vaccination - may have begun, though preliminary exchanges suggest that UK ministers are justifying the policies pursued in early 2001 still and may not be prepared to open their minds sufficiently to achieve the global solutions necessary for meat production and farm welfare to be humanely reconciled. The pressure for that must be maintained.

We have divided this final report under three headings: Handling the Outbreak, Handling any Future Outbreak, and Looking to the Future - which

last must involve the socio-economic well-being of those who live and work in the Devon countryside. However, even the first two chapters contain findings which have a bearing on the future of farming and food.

Many of our findings were not difficult to write down because to so many, who experienced or observed the events, actions and inaction of the spring and summer in Devon, they seem obvious. However, the whole area of human distress, and the efforts of those who strove to ameliorate it at the time and on the spot, is a continuing concern and about which reporting is a problem. The time and energy applied by priests, teachers and volunteers from organisations such as the Farm Crisis Network, to listening and counselling cannot be too highly praised. We wish to register gratitude for all their work on behalf of all Devonians.

Those who have written, those who attended and those who followed proceedings via the media and the Internet are all aware of the emotional atmosphere which surrounded the exposure of personal tragedy. There are also undoubtedly those who have not yet found it possible to express their feelings in writing or in person. What follows is necessarily for the present purpose as objective and pragmatic as we can make it, but none who have suffered should be in any doubt that their experience and their present plight is not diminished in any way by that. All that we have registered about the outbreak and its handling in 2001 is in some way aimed at reducing, if not removing, the risk that that experience might be repeated.

Ian Mercer
31 December 2001

Thanks are due to all my colleagues on the Committee of Inquiry and whose names are recorded in Appendix 1. They shared the emotional burden as well as extending the interrogation. We would all thank the Chief Executive of the County Council and his staff, who analysed the submissions and did everything necessary to ensure that the public hearings went as smoothly as they did. I wish to thank particularly Peter Doyle and Hilary Allison for their professional attention to the whole area of communications, Simon Timms for his work on Voices From Devon, Chris Williams for his design skills and especially Brian Wilkinson who has acted throughout well beyond the call of duty and in all respects was the Secretary of the Inquiry.

1. Handling the Outbreak

National Boundary

1.1 While it is certain that the disease entered this county via sheep bought by a Devon dealer from Longtown market in Cumbria, how it entered Britain is still a matter of conjecture. What is clear is that food is different from other internationally traded commodities and must be treated as such. It is fundamental to our existence, perishable and climate sensitive. No country or region can hope to meet consumer demand entirely from within its own boundaries. All of which means that while it is inevitable that food will be traded internationally and within national borders, it requires sensitive handling and rigorous bio-security. It was suggested to the Inquiry that import controls of meat and other livestock products at the points of entry are inadequate and below the standard in countries free from Foot and Mouth Disease (FMD).

1.2 **We find that methods of import control of travellers bringing meat products into the country in hand and hold luggage at ports and airport must be tightened by HM Customs and Excise to the highest international standards and they must have additional staffing to enforce this stricter inspection regime.**

1.3 **We also find that on a larger scale bulk imports of contaminated meat and meat products could enter the country due to regulation loopholes which allow undeclared meat to be imported fraudulently in non-meat consignments. We therefore support moves to assist Port Health Authority and Customs and Excise staff by amalgamating all meat and non-meat regulations, establishing an electronic database for Port Health officers and enhancing search powers for those officers.**

Spread of the Disease

1.4 The spread of the disease in the United Kingdom was aided by the transportation of livestock around the country. Dealing outside the ring at critical large markets appeared to make the tracing of animals more difficult if not impossible. We were told by the NFU witness that the announcement of a nationwide livestock movement ban some days after the outbreak had begun meant that the expansion of the outbreak became inevitable. At the same time some submissions indicated that it would be unwise to interfere with the traditional process that has had stock migrating from the hills to the lowlands for finishing for centuries. But for the last 50 years the policy of paying support to farmers for the number of livestock on their land, irrespective of the environmental impact, has greatly increased animal movements as farmers adjust their own numbers in the run up to the 'counting day', currently the 1st March.

1.5 **We find that there should be an immediate ban on animal movements from Day One of any future outbreak.**

1.6 **We find that, while acknowledging the practical and financial difficulties that may arise, a permanent regulation should be made requiring that all livestock which is susceptible to FMD, which moves onto a farm or returns to a farm unsold from market, or is rejected by a slaughterhouse, triggers a 21 day standstill for all relevant livestock on that holding. Exceptions could be permitted by licence which would include special conditions (e.g. quarantine, to slaughter, to holdings in the same occupancy).**

1.7 **We find that in principle a new culture needs to be developed around the marketing of livestock which effectively reduces or even eliminates trading outside the ring, the subsequent hawking of animals around the country and them changing hands a number of times in a very short period.** (These may be long established practices but are clearly the prime cause of the difficulty in tracing stock and thus the spreading of disease.) Other countries demonstrate that this kind of dealing is not an essential part of a successful livestock industry. In any case every 'middleman' transaction increases the difference between the price to the farmer and the price to the ultimate consumer. (It has been represented to us that 'dealers' are not licensed and despite the difficulty of defining 'dealing' perhaps that would improve the 'culture'.) **Regulations should be introduced that cause all buyers and sellers to register all transactions as well as movements immediately (there is currently a 3 day period of grace!). Multi-agency enforcement should accompany the regulation, and powers given to courts to ban individuals from trading if they are shown to have consistently failed to make and keep the necessary records. There is a particular need to** improve the means of identification and regulation which will better control the movement and traceability of sheep.

1.8 **We find that a study should be made of the feasibility of re-establishing the right density of local abattoirs and grant aid needed for that. The objective should be to enhance attempts to boost local consumer loyalty and reduce 'food miles'. Parallel efforts should be made to persuade large supermarkets who currently invest in a few large abattoirs that the same investment should be redirected to a network of small abattoirs instead, as a demonstration of their support for locally produced and processed meat.**

Vets and Vaccination

1.9 There is evidence that the State Veterinary Service (SVS) had been run down over the last two decades and was thus greatly overstretched during the outbreak and its aftermath, the Inquiry was told, while the knowledge and experience of many local vets was not used. Retired vets, some with experience of previous outbreaks, volunteered their services but were rebuffed. In some cases the eventual hiring of vets from other countries, while very welcome at the time, created new problems arising from a lack of local knowledge and unfamiliarity with the language. (Since our public hearing a vet who worked in both the 1967 and the 2001 outbreaks has published his recorded comparisons of the methodology employed in each, including the time taken for similar actions. It underlines all that we have heard and provides factual support for some of the evidence offered to us (Richardson, A., Veterinary Times, 5th November 2001). An explanation of the policy decisions which drove the outbreak handling up such a different route in 2001 must be sought if the disaster is not to be repeated).

1.10 **We find that the State Veterinary Service should be restored to a level which would enable it to respond more effectively to a future outbreak, and that the principle of 'retained vets' as Licensed Veterinary Inspectors should be enhanced so as to make them readily available to supplement the SVS force in any location in times of disease outbreak. We were told that precise precedent exists in other countries such as Australia and New Zealand and we can think of no good reason why such a scheme does not exist here.**

1.11 **All 'retained vets' should undergo regular training and refresher courses in the handling of animal disease epidemics.**

1.12 On vaccination, there are two potential ways in which it might be used in a future outbreak, namely for eradication and containment. **We find that the Government should set aside its perceived presumption against vaccination and explore how modern vaccination techniques could help tackle future outbreaks without resorting to the disastrous policy of killing and of contiguous culls with its attendant disposal problems that during 2001 brought both farming and tourism to their knees.**

1.13 **To this end we suggest that Government give much greater priority to more scientific research into vaccination backed with appropriate funds and contracts.**

1.14 **While we welcome the move by Government (since our Inquiry) to set up an international conference to discuss vaccination, it should go further and initiate international co-operation (beyond the EU) on vaccination by setting up an international partnership that would explore the issues, agree best practice, co-operate in vaccine development and production, and adopt a global strategy to which all livestock producing countries could sign up. This alone will create the level playing field for all producers.**

1.15 But, in the short term, the use of vaccination to contain the disease and thus reduce the pressure on the system of slaughtering and disposal must be considered.

1.16 **We find that the whole question of using vaccination in the interest of temporary containment must be explored in the context of 1.12 above. DEFRA should recognise that farmers routinely inject stock as part of their livestock husbandry. The ridiculous and dangerous situation brought about by attempts at last-minute training of vaccinators at Hatherleigh should never be repeated because there are clear alternatives.**

Culling and Disposal

1.17 Many witnesses concurred in their opposition to the so called 'contiguous cull' which was imposed on Devon farms after the toing and froing of the weekend of 24/25th March (when policy about it appeared to change four times). No one argued against the culling of identified 'dangerous contacts', but the arbitrary and pedantic way in which 'contiguousness' was determined on maps in remote offices called the whole exercise into question, and it had horrifying consequences for many farms. That and the reports received by the Inquiry of insensitive and even belligerent operatives and bungled culls do little to enhance the professional reputation of all those involved, from Ministers downwards. Culling on or beyond confirmed infected farms should be confined to dangerous animal contacts identified on the ground by vets (see 1.18 below). The actual process of killing animals must in any case be handled more sensitively and more humanely. The inquiry heard graphic descriptions of grossly incompetent attempts at slaughter so exposed that amateur videos were able to be made of the events in Knowstone parish by witnesses. Extracts were shown on national TV broadcasts.

1.18 **We find that contiguous culling should be confined to 'dangerous contacts' identified by vets on the ground, and then only after vaccination has ensured that slaughter rate and disposal rate can be reconciled. The evidence presented to us is overwhelmingly critical of the balance of effective need against unnecessary killing of healthy stock under the contiguous cull policy as carried out by MAFF (after modification on 24/25 March), and we so find.**

1.19 **We find that training in slaughter management is needed. It should include clear instruction in the assessment of the likely impact that slaughtering will have on farmers, their families and other witnesses of it. This of course will not be necessary if slaughter is discontinued in future policies. It also seemed strange to the Inquiry that amateurs were used in spite of experienced and trained slaughtermen being available.**

1.20 The disposal of animal carcasses featured in a large number of submissions and we are aware of the miscalculations which led to the creation of the still unused pit at Ash Moor, its capital cost and continuing maintenance expenditure which we deal with in paragraph 1.21 below, but there were still large numbers of carcasses to be dealt with. While we accept and support the Environment Agency's established order of preference for disposal, namely render, burial and burn, the availability of all facilities clearly proved a stumbling block in the speedy removal of carcasses from farms. We understand that rendering plants are few and far between and that even maximum use of current facilities would be unable to deal with the vast numbers

involved in this crisis. However, on-farm burial was not seen to be given serious local consideration in specific cases, and we do understand, in recording that, that the integrity of ground water in the vicinity of a burial must be maintained. Though in that respect we were concerned to learn that in a large area of north west Devon there was no comprehensive record of private sources of water (apparently quite legitimately) with consequent effects upon the task of identifying 'safe' burial sites - or other potential pollution sources for that matter.

1.21 **We do not find in favour of large-scale burials and the problems relating to the siting, construction, cost and aftermath in human terms of the Ash Moor Pit project at Petrockstowe drive us to this conclusion. That the pit cost £5.6 million to construct, costs £20,000 per week to maintain and is empty, says a great deal about the miscalculation of carcass numbers and the subsequent misapplication of public money that the handling of the Devon outbreak involved. The effect on the local community is all the more regrettable given that the pits were in fact clearly not needed. (Explanations for decisions made are still needed and restoration of the site is vital if confidence is to be restored in the way bureaucratic decisions affecting the human environment are made). Small, on-farm burials must be given more careful consideration than was apparent from the witnesses we heard.**

1.22 **If the slaughter policy survives and rendering and small on-farm burial capacity is exceeded, then locations for large-scale burials must have already been identified and published in any future contingency planning. It is vital that full and open consultation must be undertaken with the public and local authorities, including an Environmental Impact Statement (EIS), as part of a Crown Notification of Proposed Development (NOPD) if the problems that have been associated with these sites are to be avoided. The crisis that a major outbreak generates is not an excuse for Government and its agencies to override the welfare of individuals or communities or to ignore the long established rules for the management of the environment. As in the contiguous culling operation, the insensitive treatment of individuals and communities confronted by events outside their control did nothing to foster a united front or provide community leadership against the common enemy - the disease itself.**

1.23 Burning of carcasses on huge pyres was described to us as "barbaric and medieval" which is certainly the image that was conveyed. We recognise that the urgent need for disposal at the time may have been weighed against the effect on the environment and those communities living in the vicinity. But the disastrous effect of television and newspaper images of the pyres on tourism and other businesses, both nationally and internationally, certainly was not given any consideration in advance.

1.24 We were persuaded that particulate matter, spread from pyres in poor weather conditions, might well have contributed to the spread of the disease. **We find that large-scale pyres should never be used again and if burning persists as an available tool then the use of numerous, small-scale, high temperature pyres must be tested and adopted if found viable.**

1.25 As we have seen in 1.21, the volume of carcasses involved in Devon in 2001 and its gross miscalculation in advance on at least one occasion revolves around two things: the so-called contiguous cull and the separate welfare motive for culling. The contiguous cull (based on a computer model) appears to have been implemented by officials poring over maps in remote offices so that only holdings were considered, not the topography, the disposition of animals upon it nor the distances between them. One witness described the process as "carnage by computer". In many cases according to farmers and vets the risk of transmission was nil, yet all the animals on contiguous holdings were slaughtered.

1.26 **Any future cull adopted to contain the spread of disease must be applied by experienced local trained operators who act on decisions made by locally-based vets, after assessing the risk according to local information and to the physical conditions as they apply at the time (as they were in 1967).**

Animal and Human Welfare

1.27 We hope that sufficient thought applied to the whole area of animal welfare brought about by movement restrictions applied in a blanket fashion could resolve the tragic problems that it caused. This should especially preclude any future need for culling simply on welfare grounds and serves only to underline the blunt instrument which movement restriction at the extremely local level became.

1.28 **We find that it should not be beyond the combined wit of DEFRA, the Police, Highways Authorities, the RSPCA and local vets to arrange and supervise, if necessary, movements, across roads for example, to maintain health and safety among lambing flocks and calving cows in all cases where there is no risk of contagion. Powers for closing roads to enable stock movement are already within the remit of the above organisations.**

1.29 **We find that a national contingency plan should recognise the need for community support and part of the plan should be dedicated to enhancing local support networks and making adequate funds available to support their activities during times of crisis.**

Form D Movement Restriction

1.30 Farmers living under DEFRA's Form D restrictions on animal movements are the forgotten victims of this whole tragedy. There were 4,500 in this position in Devon alone. They had no prospect of trade, they had pressing animal welfare problems and for those that remained under restriction, the prospect of worse to come as winter loomed, and yet they have received not a penny in compensation.

1.31 **The Government must provide rapid financial assistance to farmers and their families on Form D restrictions.**

1.32 **The Government could, if the will was there, devise a method for providing financial assistance to farmers and their families who were on Form D restrictions. (It is not acceptable simply to say 'it is not government policy to provide compensation for consequential losses...' (DEFRA answer to Q.7, Annex 4). The whole purpose of this exercise is to get government to change policies, and slaughter is a consequence which is compensated).**

1.33 **A possible way forward could be for DEFRA to create a comprehensive list of all farmers who were subject to Form D restrictions (except perhaps some dairymen) - to include the period for which the restriction was in force. Compensation payments could then be based on a daily rate relating to the number of livestock on the farm during the period that the restriction was in force (example with simply illustrative numbers: 100 days x 100 animals x 50p per animal day = £5,000). It would be necessary to restrict the definition of 'livestock' to say cattle, sheep and pigs - with a different rate for each** type of animal. The procedure should be comparatively straightforward to administer as the livestock numbers would be supported by records.

1.34 In addition, a farmer ought to be able to show what he would have sold in normal circumstances and the Government could reimburse him the difference between that and what he has since received together with the interest accrued. This option would also apply to the non Form D farmers who were financially affected by restrictions and should compensate for losses due to beef animals ageing beyond 30 months.

Public Access

1.35 More than one witness involved in the process of closure told us that the blanket ban on the use of public rights of way or open access land such as Dartmoor and Exmoor was in retrospect a mistake, although based on regulation by the then Ministry of Agriculture, Fisheries and Food, itself based on scientific advice. This led to the "Devon is Closed" tag and had a catastrophic effect on tourism and associated industries. It was, we recognise, in the absence of a risk assessment system, an understandable immediate reaction to the need to contain disease and remove all unnecessary risks. The psychological benefits at the time were clear but with hindsight were outweighed by the longer term situation.

1.36 We find that more research is needed on the transport of the Foot and Mouth virus by boots, clothing, tyres, hooves and any other passive agent so that the degree of selection which might be applied to the closure of rights of way and the type of access may be determined to enable supportable local decisions to be made.

1.37 Until that is done, those managing access, unitary, county and national park authorities aided by parish councils should be trusted to apply restrictions in line with veterinary advice in a pragmatic way. This could be done via joint liaison groups set up as part of the contingency plan, which might be an extension of the function of local access fora (under the Countryside and Rights of Way Act 2000) in times of emergency.

2.Handling any Future Outbreak

Contingency Planning

2.1 It was not obvious to us from the evidence received that MAFF was working to any form of coherent contingency plan. We now know from DEFRA that there was a 'largely internal' plan which, it is confessed, was overtaken by the scale and size of the outbreak. That tells its own story. Lessons, which should have been learned from the outbreak in 1967, did not appear to have been implemented and recommendations of the official report into that outbreak were not applied. Moving from the strategic to the tactical position, we were easily persuaded that local knowledge was not sought and was dismissed when proffered. The assertion by one witness that "Strangers don't work well" in local situations caught our imagination. For instance in navigating lorries from distant bases, parish knowledge could have avoided a huge waste of energy and time. This knowledge should also be taken into account in the risk assessment of rights of way by those responsible for decisions on closure.

2.2 **We find that a new National Contingency Plan, such as that produced for maritime pollution response by the Marine and Coastguard Agency, needs to be developed quickly, given wide consultation among all the appropriate parties and then published. Publication should be by all available means and not confined to the Internet to which many farmers and parish clerks, for instance, do not have access. It should identify the organisations that will be involved in the response to a Foot and Mouth Disease outbreak in a County or Unitary Authority area, explain their responsibilities and the ways they will work together. An adequate plan to deal with any scale of epidemic needs to be 'owned' by all who have and should have a role in handling it. It should be part of an emergency planning process that involves all of them in its construction, testing and regular rehearsal. It must recognise the fundamental need for clear information and effective two-way communications. It must cascade down via the region to the county, the district and particularly to the parish. Responsibilities at each of those levels for implementing allocated functions should be set out (e.g. County Council for trading standards, highways (including public rights of way), and environmental planning,**

District for environmental health, and Parishes should up date emergency plans adapting them for the easy transmission of local knowledge to incomers). The National Contingency Plan should be reviewed, tested and rehearsed every 5 years, and at local levels at lesser intervals.

Command and Control

2.3 It was made clear to the Inquiry that such a plan and its cascade should determine how command and control is exercised. In Devon, as elsewhere, it soon became clear that MAFF did not have among its ranks those who could lead operations in the field. It is of course the prerogative of Ministers to determine and instigate policy after due advice from appropriate sources, but the Contingency Plan should be implemented nationally by someone able to command respect and with experience of managing emergency operations. But action on the ground in all senses must be in the hands of those used to command and with a sufficient support system to be effective. Much was made to us of the contrast of achievement between a Brigadier in Cumbria and a Major in Devon. Experience must be a factor in that, but Brigadiers also bring systems (brigades) with them, command is understood, respect is shown externally and much else flows from those characteristics. The Chief Constable explained his emergency control system to us and indicated his frustration at the limitations the military authority appeared to apply to itself (in contrast to the Cumbrian situation). He clearly would have been happier in control, but also made it clear that 'that time is long past'. In any case it is equally clear that the constabulary has a full time job to do in normal times and that job does not diminish during crises of this long duration. Available military manpower is on the other hand able to detach itself from training and ceremonial to concentrate on the temporary job in hand. The role of the police in upholding the law (even against other parts of the civil power) and in movement control during disease outbreaks of this kind is nevertheless a critical component of a Contingency Plan.

2.4 **We find that in the field handling all the operational consequences of combating the disease there would best be a military command, at least at brigadier level, from Day One of the outbreak. He or she should work closely** alongside the Chief Constable whose roles are already clearly defined and should have environmental and veterinary aides at his or her elbow.

Communication

2.5 The Inquiry heard that a culture of secrecy was perceived within MAFF, public communication was poor to non-existent, and this led to an atmosphere of suspicion, confusion, changing advice and inconsistencies. This in turn was reflected by farmers, the media and other organisations with which the Ministry had dealings.

2.6 **We find that from Day One open two-way communication must begin within the operational organisation and with all third parties. It is vital that timely and accurate information is provided to individuals and communities likely to be affected in an outbreak. This must include farmers and all those who provide local support and advice such as parish clergy.**

2.7 **Effective communications must therefore be at the heart of any emergency response for that response to be successful. It is essential that efficient two-way communications are recognised in advance as being central to the effectiveness of any contingency planning and rigorously tested in regular local, regional and national exercises.**

2.8 **Communication planning must involve all organisations required to deal with any future outbreak. There must be, however, professional management of a communications 'control centre' within the structure of the overall command. Within that context, each organisation must have a plan for its own communicating responsibilities and must consult partner agencies to ensure that all the information which it dispenses is up-to-date, consistent and recognises each agency's specific role and responsibilities.**

2.9 The media can be an important source of public information and could greatly assist in the dissemination of accurate information. But the media, like nature, abhors a vacuum and, in the absence of official information, will be filled from alternative sources, including rumour. All information must be clear, open and honest, and political considerations should be set aside. **The media should be involved in communications planning and exercises.**

2.10 The good lessons learned from the preparation for and response to the multi-agency communications for the 1999 Eclipse and, to a lesser extent, the Millennium Bug need to be adopted and adapted. **We therefore find that contingency planning should include provision for county (or regional as appropriate) communications centres staffed by specialists from the organisations involved and should identify suitable venues which can be activated speedily. Such centres need to make the best use of broadcast media - television, radio and Internet - and it is essential that a proactive partnership is established with media organisations to achieve this goal.**

Legal Issues

2.11 We heard from one professional witness that MAFF/DEFRA exceeded the limits of legislation current during the outbreak and undertook actions for which there was little or no legal power granted. This was especially the case in connection with

- limited powers to slaughter animals on contiguous farms, the "contiguous cull" policy;

- limited powers in relation to the taking of blood samples;

- the unlawful construction of the Ash Moor pits without planning permission and insufficient consultation with the local planning authority;

- the breach of MAFF's own guidelines in actions such as the temporary storage of carcasses on farms and at pyre sites, liable to cause pollution of surface and ground water (the role of the Environment Agency in these actions was questioned by one witness);

- statutory nuisance caused by pyres (other than smoke) which, it was said did not apply to MAFF during a time of emergency. This was not in fact the case.

There were other dubious statements by MAFF/DEFRA, for example that the co-operation of farmers was needed for a vaccination policy to operate (not so) or, where operations were organised on behalf of MAFF by the Ministry of Defence, the MoD became liable for environmental damage (again, not so).

We find that if it is contemplated that future epidemics must be tackled in the same way as in 2001 then the existing statutory provisions should be urgently reviewed in consultation

with all those bodies whose functions are involved to ensure that an unequivocally clear and properly stocked arsenal is in place to legitimise that response.

Research Now

2.12 We summarise below the areas where we have found substantial lack of knowledge and where research, therefore, needs to be undertaken with urgency:

- the cost benefit comparison of preventing the arrival and spread of the disease with the handling of the outbreak and eliminating the disease after that;

- vaccination for both continuous protection against an outbreak and for containment of an outbreak;

- risk assessment of the use of the public access network in each highway authority area and national park;

- transmission of FM virus(es) by all the possible vectors but especially inanimate ones such as boots, anoraks or tyres;

- separating and refining animal movement control for different purposes such as finishing stock from the hill, for trade, for containing the disease, for lambing and calving and for other animal welfare reasons.

3. Looking to the Future

Recovery in Devon

3.1 The outbreak of Foot and Mouth in Devon soon brought into the sharpest relief the interdependence of farming and what is generalised as tourism but includes all aspects of human enjoyment of its environment. Indeed, the interaction of both with all aspects of rural life and work were revealed more starkly and to a wider audience than ever before. While industries upstream and downstream from farming itself were predictably affected greatly, all kinds of rural and rurally-based trades found themselves without their normal customers. Jobbing builders could not go on to farms, craftsmen had no shows at which to sell, and many a retailer discovered how much his village trade was supplemented by the regular visitor whose target may have been a moorland walk but who bought meat or cheese from a favourite shop on the way home. Village teashops and guesthouses saw trade after the spring half term die right away, and farmers who had diversified (as advised) into a visitor's service of some kind were dealt a double whammy as booking cancellations were added to their inability to carry out any other kind of transaction. At the same time, the portrayal by the media of what appeared to be happening throughout the countryside was seen to affect potential and actual custom in towns and on the coast, as well as for rurally-based businesses.

3.2 The clear need for the earliest recovery of the socio-economic well-being of Devon focused the attention of the County Council as soon as the scale of the crisis was perceived. It attracted support for its Devon Recovery Plan from 150 partners including Government departments, their agencies and many Non-Government Organisations (NGOs). We have welcomed Lord Haskins' ready endorsement of that Plan.

3.3 Much of the 10 point Plan looks beyond the recovery phase. That for agriculture sets the tone:

> establishing a long term vision for the future of Devon's agriculture, the capacity to deliver it and a development programme to help the industry adopt more sustainable practices, including the marketing of local produce, organic farming, co-operative ventures, forestry, horticulture, new local abattoirs, local processing and renewable energy.

3.4 More of the 10 points have longer term implications. They are: marketing the 'Devon brand', health and welfare support, environmental multiple benefits and new initiatives relating to access.

3.5. This Inquiry's terms of reference (Appendix 2) includes at ii:

> The creation of a sustainable, competitive and diverse farming and food sector which in turn contributes to a thriving and sustainable rural economy and advances environmental health and animal welfare goals.

The findings of the Inquiry in those respects and which relate to the longer term future of the countryside of Devon are summarised below.

The Agricultural Perspective

3.6 The agricultural environment of Devon remains one in which, despite global climate variation, grass is the most significant and optimum crop and livestock conversion of it the sensible core of food production in the bulk of the county. Young stock for finishing, meat, milk and their derivatives are our most competitive products in a fair free market.

3.7 We feel it necessary to register in passing that even those product categories vary in the context of competition. The next World Trade Organisation (WTO) round and the extension of the European Union (EU) eastward will probably increase that variation and thus the need for even more careful selection by the producer of what works best for him or her. As we said at the beginning, food needs to be treated differently from other commodities in WTO terms. Temperate countries need to be able to satisfy their home markets to the greatest possible degree, in that which they produce best, and export their surplus specialities. We say this here only because DEFRA's own figures show how great is the imbalance for the UK in so much of the relevant trade. (Exporting milk powder - lowest value dairy product - and importing yoghurt - high value - is the classic example). It is considerably less than a lifetime ago that the British Isles was providing its own domestic vegetables and fruit in season (and we have lost that component of the variety of life geared to land and time of year). DEFRA's figures also show that wheat and even bread and dough cross the Channel in both directions, as do beef, lamb and pork. These contradictory movements are in remarkably similar quantities which, if reduced to the difference between them, would save a substantial proportion of the food miles an average British meal costs. Of course there are other factors at work but working with nature is an important base for sustainable land use and food production as pre-refrigeration and prairie times proved.

3.8   However, the basic grass/stock formula in paragraph 3.6 implies a landscape for livestock, and thus dominated, below 300 metres OD (sea level), by medium-sized fields right for stock management and shelter functions, with variation where appropriate soil, slope and aspect encourage arable working for animal feed production. Devon banks and their summit hedges and small copses will also have a continuing role. In turn that implies that while average farm holding size may increase as landowner numbers change, perceived patterns in the countryside need not change in general terms. Thus the well-loved Devon pastoral landscape should persist and so, therefore, will the demand for maintenance of all its singular characteristics.

3.9   To these ends, **we find that Government (and EU) spending and support patterns in the Devon countryside should reflect the need to achieve two things: the further development and sustaining of a quality livestock produce industry; and an adequate labour force. The latter is required to achieve more sophisticated stock management, more added value on or close to the farm and more detailed environmental quality maintenance. Principles agreed already to these ends within Common Agricultural Policy reform need to be pursued with more urgency and with the overt motive of accelerating change.**

3.10   **We find that developing the marketing of quality Devon farm products (within the `Devon Brand') should be pursued vigorously with the avowed intent of developing a local loyalty to a far greater degree than presently exists. Then market extension must be sought regionally and where appropriate nationally, building in all three cases upon existing successful enterprise. The most successful of these already demonstrate the virtues of co-operative finishing and trading, and this will be critical if destructive over-competition is not to damage the natural evolution of the new value-adding farming. (There is a limit to the number of similar enterprises which any locality can support).**

The Workforce

3.11   **We find that sustaining a comprehensive livestock industry from breeding and store production in the hills to finishing animals and producing the whole range of dairy products to the quality level a modern society requires, will in the end demand a larger labour force than presently deployed. Prices paid by the customer, reduction in the middlemen's 'cut', and support funds from Government will have to reflect that.**

3.12   **While that workforce properly lead and managed could also maintain the well-loved detail of the farmed landscape, the increased demands generated by environmental and biodiversity improvement objectives and obligations will further increase the labour required. Contractors, who have become an integral part of the agricultural scene over the last 50 years, will doubtless have an extended role here.**

3.13   **Relating the public support referred to in 3.11 above to 3.12, a headage payment for stockmen and lengthmen is no longer necessarily a joke. Some clever agri-environment experiments and management agreements have already shown an increase of such specialists on the farm and in the contracting ranks. It is claimed that enjoyment of such work and its contribution to self-fulfilment have increased at the same time. It goes without saying that a labour force requires to be housed, but any commentary on the future of the countryside anywhere in Britain cannot avoid reference to the need for affordable housing in both bought and rented sectors. The reinstatement of rural 'council' housing on the countryside management agenda would show that government recognised a policy vacuum that needs to be filled.**

3.14 **We find that these future demands for more sophisticated labour (ironically with historic as well as new technological skills) imply new goals for training and recruitment. In turn they require new approaches to the integration of agricultural and environmental skills in further and higher education. Colleges must develop the required courses for combined operations on the farm if succeeding generations of farmers are to deliver what the paying public customer needs. Family farm succession is significant, because the delivery of sustainable farming, forestry and landscape demands stable management strategies that extend further into the future than a generation.**

Support Schemes and Public Goods

3.15 Government agencies and non-Government organisations underlined these needs and proposed to us 'new' models for the public purchase of environmental goods and services. Some of them have already been tested, the most useful one (Tir Cymen) in three districts, or 10% of Wales for some 8 or 9 years now, and while its all-Wales successor (Tir Gofal) is an endorsement of its success, some values have been lost in the extension. Similarly, management agreements under the Wildlife and Countryside Act of 1981 proved more sophisticated and flexible than the bureaucratic Environmentally Sensitive Area (ESA) and Countryside Stewardship systems are now. Those who live close to these schemes now pleaded, before us, for much greater flexibility in them.

3.16 **We find that a more flexible approach to these and any new schemes which allows operational plan-making on the farm and ensures that the plan integrates food, fibre and environmental outputs, should be sought. This demands a consensus between agricultural and environmental agencies in both public and private sectors if the farmer is to get sensibly balanced advice and help which he or she can turn into practical and profitable application.**

3.17 **We find that the integration of quality food and fibre production with recognised environmental outputs should be the ambition of a new farmer-culture. That culture shift (universally assumed, as opposed to the scattered shining examples already with us) is best begun at the educational and training level where new courses (as we have said above) should be devised to achieve the integration.**

3.18 However, the farming industry has always readily accepted advice usually linked to incentives. It has always shared experience and more recently on-the-job training. Thus a high proportion of the present generation of farmers is not necessarily immune from cultural change in its own time if the right resources are made available. **Most are just now peering for the light at the end of a tunnel and advantage should be taken of that.**

3.19 We are aware that headage payments, at least in terms of the Hill Livestock Compensatory Allowance (HLCA), are being phased out, and replaced by area payments (HFA). In the interests of a sustainable agriculture the principle could well be extended and not confined to the hills.

3.20 **We find that all livestock farming support systems should be devised so that numbers of stock are no longer the basic criterion for any relevant formula - in the lowland as well as the hills.**

3.21 It was suggested to us that sustainability in farming is, and should remain, underpinned by the concept of the family farm (see also 3.14) and, despite 3.8, a variation in holding size would probably ensure the persistence of certain qualities in the landscape. In both respects support and regulatory systems need to take account of the desirable end. They also need to assimilate the variation in the agricultural potential of the land in question as expressed in the grading of that land.

3.22 **We find that the basic payments in any tiered system of agri-environment support should be tied to long established grades of agricultural land quality on a sliding scale. Within each grade, thresholds relating to holding area should be applied to favour the smaller but viable farm.**

Access

3.23 The network of local roads and rights of way is critical to farmers, the services they require in both delivery and collection, to other countrymen and to the visiting public. The Foot and Mouth epidemic and its handling in respect of movement restriction on and off farms and of public recreation highlighted that in many different ways.

3.24 **We find that a rare opportunity now exists to enhance and refine, with public support, the network of footpaths, bridleways, cycleways, byways and unclassified roads in the interests of** reconciling farm and livestock management and enjoyment of the countryside.

3.25 **The day-to-day management of access for leisure, exercise and the welfare of animals (in general and during future crises) must also be greatly improved. That demands increases in the application of money and manpower to it by all the relevant authorities. It probably also implies delegation of that management by Highway Authorities where there is other competence to hand in the interests of speedy action and deploying available manpower more effectively.**

Visiting the Countryside

3.26 It is clear that many businesses outside the farming industry suffered greatly as a result of the FMD crisis and its handling. Many are part of rural communities' essential structure - shops, post offices, builders and all the allied trades - and the extent of that suffering will not be clear until well into next summer. They in turn, and with some farmers, depend upon the visiting public, popularly: tourists.

3.27 Like agriculture, the tourism industry is made up of a vast number of operations, varying greatly in size. It depends upon representative groupings and agencies to produce anything approaching corporate action or lobbying. Yet its enormous variety is its lifeblood. Farmers have been urged to diversify and their easiest other option is some form of tourism or visitor servicing. Those well into the combined activities of farming and tourism were dealt a double whammy by the consequences of the Foot and Mouth outbreak.

3.28 **We find that tourist industry representatives should be included in the local and national contingency plan preparation to which we have referred in 2.2 and especially its access management arrangements. They should also be recipients of all information from Day One in communications planning.**

3.29 **We also find that tourist operators and accommodation providers across the spectrum should have access to timely and accurate information to help prepare their own advice for visitors in advance so that a welcome, despite a disease epidemic, can still be offered and activated.**

Financial Management

3.30 It is clear to us that the future health and well-being of society would be enhanced by what we have found. We acknowledge that much of what we have concluded and written under this heading only confirms that which many rural thinkers have argued for some time. Indeed, we have recorded that some good models for the public purchase of environmental benefits have also been tested. But to achieve the improvement necessary in the contribution which the countryside makes to British society through food and fibre production and the opportunities for all forms of recreation there must be a reorganisation of spending.

3.31 **We find that that reorganisation applies to the individual through prices paid and taxes tolerated, and to the corporate will through government at all levels from the European Union to District Councils. 'Reorganisation of spending' includes increases in the funds applied in the right places and decreases in the bureaucratic complexity involved. This complexity has been shown in the last few months to distort grossly the routes, and time taken for funds provided, to reach the point of application on the ground. The process of applying the FMD Business Support Fund by some Regional Development Agencies appears to us to have been a case in point. It seems to us that the bureaucratic regulatory processes by which EU funds, for instance, are drawn down and applied to work on the ground in the UK are much more complex and inhibitory than in other close neighbour countries. Such complexity frustrates worthy action and diminishes the available funds by absorbing them into administrative costs.**

Afterword

3.32 The Secretary of State said before a Parliamentary Committee in mid October 2001 that it would be a miracle if FMD was finally over. The more reason therefore that the Government now swiftly plans how to deal effectively and efficiently with any future outbreak or resurgence. We believe that this report is 'the voice of Devon' after the crisis. We intend that it should not fall on deaf ears.

APPENDIX 1

Members of the Devon Inquiry Committee

Professor Ian Mercer CBE
Professor Mercer was the first Chief Executive of the Countryside Council for Wales. In 1995 he became the first Secretary General of the Association of National Park Authorities, a position he held until his retirement in 2001.

Cllr Nolan Clarke
Devon County Councillor for Bovey Tracey (Liberal Democrat)

Cllr Christine Marsh
Devon County Councillor for Okehampton Rural (Conservative)

Cllr Richard Westlake
Devon County Councillor for Exeter Stoke Hill and Polsloe (Labour)

Cllr Roger Giles
Devon County Councillor for Ottery St Mary Rural (Independent)

Cllr David Poole
Torridge District Councillor for the Waldon Ward (Independent)

Cllr Peter Hill
West Devon Borough Councillor for the Chagford Ward (Independent)

Cllr Eric Ley
North Devon District Councillor for the parishes of Bishops Nympton, East Anstey, Knowstone, Molland, Twitchen and West Anstey (Independent)

APPENDIX 2

Terms of Reference of the Devon Foot and Mouth Inquiry

To conduct an investigation in public into the Foot and Mouth epidemic in Devon and to make recommendations to the Government's inquiries into FMD and the future of farming and the countryside for:

i)   the tackling of any future major animal disease outbreak;

ii)   the creation of a sustainable, competitive and diverse farming and food sector which contributes to a thriving and sustainable rural economy and advances environmental, economic, health and animal welfare goals.

In carrying out its task the Inquiry will take into account:

- the impact of the Foot and Mouth outbreak on the economy (including tourism), environment and health of the communities of Devon;

- the contribution the Devon Recovery Plan can make to the future reform of agriculture, food production and promotion and land use, and to the creation of a sustainable rural economy;

- the effectiveness of the various agencies involved in the response to the 2001 outbreak, their inter-relationship and relationship with local communities, and identify any constraints such as resources, communications, command and control systems, and training.

And that the findings be:

- made widely available to the public, stakeholders and key opinion formers such as MPs, MEPs and the media;

- used to support the county's bid for Government funding for the Devon Recovery Plan.

APPENDIX 3

Programme of the Devon FMD Inquiry Hearings

HELD AT COUNTY HALL, EXETER 8th –12th OCTOBER 2001

Monday, 8th October 2001 – Strategic Issues

- David Hill, Devon County Chairman, National Farmers' Union
- Jeremy Worth, SW Regional Director, The Countryside Agency
- Mary Quicke, J G Quicke and Partners (cheesesmakers)
- Tim Brooks, Devon Branch, Country Landowners and Business Association
- Simon Hodgson, South West Regional Development Agency
- Mark Tomlinson, Local Resident
- Brian Aldridge, Jo Skinner, John Pratt and Ron Dawson, Local Residents
- Colin Latham, John Martin, Edward Martin and David May, Farmers

Tuesday, 9th October 2001 - Business and Tourism

- John Varley (Estates Director) and John Bain, Clinton Devon Estates
- Alex Raeder, Senior Land Agent, Devon Region, National Trust
- Diane Lethbridge, Taste of the West
- Colin Lomax, Acting Head of Economic Development, Devon County Council
- John Fowler, Chairman, John Fowler Holidays
- Carol Hutchings, Chairman, South Devon Tourism Association
- David Andrew, Assistant Director, Environment Directorate, Devon County Council
- Malcolm Bell, Chief Executive, South West Tourism
- Richard Pringle, Stags Auctioneers and Estate Agents

Wednesday, 10th October 2001 - Health and Communities

- Mark Raven, Headteacher, Black Torrington Church of England Primary School
- Mark Goodman (County Organiser) and Les Hayward, Devon Federation of Young Farmers' Club
- Barbara Thomas, Vice-Chairman, Devon Association of Parish Councils
- Rev Paul Fitzpatrick, Northmoor Team Ministry
- Dr Nigel Stone, National Park Officer, Exmoor National Park Authority
- Tania Haycocks (Chairman) and Margaret Noon (Chairman of Organisation Sub-Committee), Devon Federation of Women's Institutes
- Brian Warren, Stephen Dennis and Peter Clarke, Farm Crisis Network
- Dr Mike Owen, Director of Public Health, North and East Devon Health Authority
- Jim Pile, Farmer
- Sir John Evans (Chief Constable) and Superintendent Mike Sarsfield, Devon and Cornwall Constabulary

Thursday, 11th October 2001 - Communication

- Hilary Allison, Peter Doyle and Brian Nute, Communications and Information, Devon County Council
- Graham Gilbert, Managing Director, Great Western Radio
- Chris Foreman, Senior Output Editor, Carlton TV
- Carol Trewin, Farming Editor, Western Morning News
- Richard Hill, Emergency Planning Service, Devon County Council
- Ken Lancaster and Alan Perryman, Kennerleigh Parish Meeting

- Sue Bizley, Citizens' Advice Bureau

- William Norman, David Morgans and Kenneth Dykes, Knowstone Parish Council

- David Incoll, Chief Executive, West Devon Borough Council, Richard Brassington, Chief Executive, Torridge District Council and Andrew Millie, Assistant Environmental Health Manager, North Devon District Council

Friday, 12th October 2001 - Environment and Animal Welfare

- Geoff Bateman (Devon Area Manager), Malcolm Chudley and Martin Booth, Environment Agency

- Dr Nick Atkinson, Chief Executive, Dartmoor National Park Authority

- Mark Robins (SW Regional Policy Officer) and Frances Winder (Agricultural Policy Officer), Royal Society for the Protection of Birds

- Roger Rivett, Head of Trading Standards, Devon County Council

- Wendy Vere, DAL Vere and Partners (veterinary surgeons)

- Clare Broom, Pro-Vice Chancellor, University of Plymouth (Seale-Hayne)

- John Tresidder, SW Regional Superintendent, RSPCA

- Phil Davies, Team Manager, Western Counties Veterinary Association

- Phil Collins, Devon Team, English Nature

- Hugh Thomas and Mal Treharne (Public Relations Director), Countryside Alliance

APPENDIX 4

Chronology of Devon County Council's Response

TO THE FOOT AND MOUTH DISEASE CRISIS IN DEVON FEBRUARY-DECEMBER 2001

"Openness and a desire to get at the facts, revealing the realities rather than the perceptions of the impact of the Foot and Mouth outbreak in Devon, have been at the core of Devon County Council's Inquiry into Foot and Mouth Disease.

"In just over two months since the Inquiry was announced at the end of July, Devon County Council has shown not just a willingness but also a determination to do something for which there seems to be little or no political appetite in Westminster – that is to hold a public inquiry into the effects of the worst human and animal health disaster to have affected Britain in decades."

Carol Trewin, Former Farming Editor,
Western Morning News

February 24

First FMD case reported in Devon. Devon County Council's Trading Standards Service duty animal health officer receives report of suspected outbreak at Highhampton from MAFF duty vet. Head of Trading Standards attends briefing at MAFF's regional HQ. Trading Standards officers despatched to the Highampton area that night and work into the early hours in driving snow serving restriction orders and erecting warning signs. Trading Standards alerts duty Media and PR officer who liaises with MAFF Press Office.

February 25

First news conference at MAFF regional HQ. Plans are made to commit the whole of the Trading Standards Service staff — around 45 officers — to provide an outbreak response team working in shifts seven days a week. Trading Standards Operations Centre and farmers' helpline set up. County Council issues emergency advice to the public and staff on minimising risk.

February 26

MAFF announces scheme allowing animals from farms outside the Infected Areas to be moved to slaughter under licences to be issued by local authorities. County Council introduces 12 point risk reduction plan including suspension of routine highway maintenance in the Infected Areas, cancellation of non-essential visits, and advice to the public on avoiding contact with farm animals and not using footpaths. All non-emergency Trading Standards work suspended, neighbouring authorities and other advice agencies warned. A County Council public information helpline is set up.

February 27

County Council sets up special Foot and Mouth advice and information website. Links to other useful sites are added as the outbreak progresses. Council urges farmers to check animal movement records to speed up tracking process and also warns farmers to halt livestock transport. MAFF publishes Order allowing local authorities to close footpaths and bridleways.

February 28

All public rights of way in rural areas of Devon — nearly 3,500 miles — are closed by the County Council, as are Country Parks. Council distributes information and closure notices to parish councils and landowners. Details and notices are also published on the Internet. Civic amenity sites are closed in Infected Areas.

March 1

County Council convenes first of a series of regular briefing meetings between senior Councillors, officers and NFU officials. Council issues the first of a series of Chief Executive's briefings to parish councils and public.

March 5

MAFF implements new licensing scheme. County Council drafts in additional staff from other units to assist Trading Standards in handling hundreds of licence applications.

March 6

County Council's Executive Committee commissions Exeter University's Agricultural Economics Unit to investigate the economic impact of Foot and Mouth. NFU Regional Director presents Executive Committee with an update. Short-term funding for agencies providing advice services to farmers is authorised. Report by Chief Executive recommends Government reconsiders the cost-effectiveness of vaccination as an alternative to slaughter.

March 12

Limited re-introduction of non-Foot and Mouth work by Trading Standards to provide some kind of service to the wider public.

March 14

Council welcomes setting up of Rural Task Force. County Leader of the Council invites Prime Minister to Devon to see impact and calls for better cross-departmental co-ordination by Government, improved communications between MAFF, local government and the farming community, and logistical expertise to speed up the disposal of slaughtered livestock.

March 16

Government introduces Order giving the power to lift public rights of way restrictions by a declaration, made either by a Minister or a local authority.

March 20

County Council calls for postponement of May elections.

March 28

County Council publicises its Holiday Line call centre and tourism website as key sources of information about what visitors can see and do in Devon despite the outbreak.

March 29

County Council's Executive Committee publishes initial findings of the Exeter University study which, based on the position at March 19, estimates up to 1,200 jobs in farming and related industries, and 8,700 jobs in the tourist industry could be lost. It also estimates a total loss of £280 million to the county's economy (equivalent to 3.5% of total Gross Domestic Product). Executive Committee instructs officers to commence work on a Devon recovery programme.

April 2

Leader of the County Council flying into London from Budapest, receives call from Chief Executive alerting him to a request for a meeting with the Prime Minister for a briefing on Foot and Mouth in Devon the following day.

April 3

Downing Street meeting. Leader briefs Prime Minister on the County Council's plans for a phased re-opening of footpaths in consultation with MAFF, NFU and landowners. He welcomes decision to postpone elections to June 7, but warns Mr Blair of the scale of the economic impact on Devon and urges him to appoint a local Task Force to co-ordinate a recovery programme.

April 5

County Council hosts the first of a series of consultation meetings with key stakeholders — NFU, CLA, MAFF, National Trust, National Parks and other landowners — on proposals for phased re-openings of the county's public rights of way network. A major consultation of local landowners is also launched. Senior Councillor Sir Simon Day calls for European aid at Committee of the Regions meeting in Brussels.

April 8

County Council launches tourism promotion campaign aimed at key audience in the Midlands. In anticipation of footpath re-openings for Easter, full page ads are taken in the *Sunday Mercury,* the largest regional Sunday paper, with the message "Rediscover the delights of Devon". The advert promotes the fact that 90 per cent of the county's attractions are open for visitors to enjoy.

April 9

Launch of "Green for Go" campaign re-opening 140 public rights of way including 25% of the coastal network in time for the Easter holiday. County Council issues guidance to the public on walking in the countryside and circulates information to tourism information centres, libraries and parishes. Advice from MAFF and the Police leads to disinfectant matting laid down by District Council being removed from roads in Mid Devon.

April 10

County Council's mobile library service is reintroduced for communities on A and B roads. Moorland routes and stops near farms remain suspended.

April 11

County Council urges Government to relax animal movement restrictions to help ease the serious livestock welfare problems.

April 12

County Council announces its Operations Centre will be open throughout Easter.

April 19

County Council holds first all-party Rural Task Group meeting with tourism and agriculture representatives to plan a recovery programme for the Devon economy. Council agrees to a series of measures including developing a draft recovery plan, leading a major tourism promotion campaign, and providing co-ordinated information on sources of benefits, grants and business advice.

April 20

County Council's Trading Standards inform farmers that new licensing arrangements mean some farms within the Infected Areas can move livestock direct to slaughter.

April 26

County Council Chief Executive joins Chief Executive of South West Tourism to brief House of Commons Culture, Media and Sports Select Committee about the impact on the tourism industry.

May 3

Ahead of the May Bank Holiday, County Council re-opens 80 public rights of way in second phase of "Green for Go" campaign. 45 per cent of the coastal footpath network is now open.

May 8

County Council launches countywide consultation on its draft £180 million Devon Recovery Plan. Followed up with detailed briefings of MEPs, Government Office South West, the Regional Development Agency, European Commission officials and local representatives on the national Foot and Mouth Rural Task Force.

May 9

In partnership with Devon's district councils, County Council tackles the concern that Foot and Mouth will lead to low turn-outs for the rescheduled elections on June 7 by launching a campaign to encourage people to take up their right to a postal vote.

May 15

County Council's Executive Committee authorises setting up a special Foot and Mouth Recovery Unit dedicated to developing and co-ordinating the recovery programme working in partnership with other agencies.

May 25

County Council calls for public inquiry into the handling of the Foot and Mouth crisis.

May 26

Following consultation with landowners and stakeholders, 1,440 footpaths and bridleways are re-opened - representing 90 per cent of the footpath network outside the Infected Areas.

June 6

Footpaths and bridleways across South Dartmoor are re-opened. Renewed guidance issued to the public on walking in the countryside.

June 7

General Election and County Council elections in Devon.

June 16

County Council scales down footpath re-openings in Mid and East Devon in response to Foot and Mouth outbreak on the Somerset border.

June 17

Last confirmed case of Foot and Mouth reported in Devon. Total number of cases in the County reaches 173. 4,500 Devon farms are under MAFF "Form D" livestock movement restrictions.

June 21

County Hall hosts Devon Recovery Plan conference attended by 150 organisations and key opinion formers, including MEPs, Government Office for the South West, Department for Environment, Food and Rural Affairs, South West Regional Development Agency, South West Tourism, the NFU and many others. Conference endorses all-party support for the £180 million Plan.

June 30

North Devon coastal footpath re-opens. News welcomed by South West Tourism. Over half the county's footpath network is now open.

July 11

County Council's Executive Chairman and Chief Executive, supported by District Council, Tourism and NFU representatives, give presentation on the Devon Recovery Plan to the Government's Rural Task Force. Rural Affairs Minister Alun Michael commends the County Council's quick action in pulling together a Recovery Plan and authorises detailed discussions with civil servants.

July 17

Updated research by Exeter University's Agricultural Economics Unit estimates the epidemic may cost the county £316 million in lost income (2.86 per cent of GDP) and puts total potential job losses over 12 months at 7,805.

July 20

Devon is one of just six authorities to be given a temporary exemption from the Government's decision to lift the blanket closure of footpaths. The decision recognises that the County Council's measured programme of re-opening footpaths in phases is aiding the county's economic recovery whilst following veterinary guidance on prudent Foot and Mouth precautions. Some 63 per cent - over 4,000 footpaths - of the county network is now open. At the request of the NFU, County Council re-issues guidance to dog walkers about walking in the countryside.

July 25

Public rights of way re-open across Exmoor National Park.

July 30

County Council's Executive gives all-party backing to holding a Devon Foot and Mouth Inquiry with an instruction that its findings be passed on to the Government and any national inquiry into the crisis. 75 per cent of Devon's footpath network is now open.

July to August

County Council issues on average 1,100 animal movement licences a week.

August 1

Infected Area status lifted in Devon.

August 9

County Council launches "Pledge For Devon" scheme at the Devon County Show (postponed from May) to encourage staff and public to pledge an action or series of actions in support of Devon's hard-hit food producers, tourist industry and the countryside in general. Council joins forces with RDA, Countryside Agency and National Parks to present the "Devon Forward" exhibition at the Show, highlighting what the county has to offer and promoting local produce. County Council gives cautious welcome to Government's announcement of three national inquiries.

August 11

Council re-opens footpaths in North and West Devon, previously the worst Foot and Mouth affected areas. 95 per cent of the network now open.

August 20

County Council launches consultation with farmers on the potential for scaling back the 7-day Licensing helpline.

August 22

Council announces Devon Foot and Mouth Inquiry with all party and District Council support. Terms of reference are published and written submissions invited. Special website and call centre is set up to handle public interest in the Inquiry.

August 23

Professor Ian Mercer CBE is announced as the independent Chairman of the Devon Inquiry.

September 3

Lord Haskins, the Government's rural recovery co-ordinator, visits Devon on a fact-finding mission. He says the Devon Inquiry will help the national investigations and commends the county's Foot and Mouth recovery partnership.

September 7

County Council's licensing helpline scaled back to six days a week (half day Saturday).

September 17

Number of licences issued by County Council on any one day peaks at 360.

September 24

Government introduces "Autumn Movement" scheme for cattle and pigs.

September 28

Closing date for Devon FMD Inquiry submissions. Some 380 submissions are received with evidence from a wide range of organisations and people from all walks of life including farmers, vets, hoteliers, holiday attraction owners, business people, MPs, MEPs, clergy, headteachers, lecturers and local councillors.

October 1

Government introduces "Autumn Movement" scheme for sheep. County Council's Trading Standards sets up new licensing centre with additional temporary staff to cope with extra workload.

October 8 - 12

The Devon Foot and Mouth Inquiry hearings in public are held at County Hall in Exeter and broadcast live via the Internet in collaboration with Eclipse and BBC Online. Fifty witnesses, including RDA, Environment Agency, NFU, Police and Countryside Agency, give evidence. Internet service receives 60,000 "hits". Widespread national and regional media coverage.

October 10

Lord Haskins publishes "Rural Recovery after Foot and Mouth Disease" coinciding with publication of the Rural Task Force's report — both documents support the aims of the Devon Recovery Plan.

October 18

County Council publishes new report, "Impact of Foot and Mouth", which says Foot and Mouth has halved the income of small firms in the worst affected areas of the county, cites research suggesting the epidemic has largely led to the loss of 3,000 jobs, and warns that small firms have not achieved the income required to sustain them through the coming winter.

October 24

DEFRA's written response to the Devon FMD Inquiry's questions is received by County Council.

October 26

Inquiry's preliminary findings are sent to Sir Don Curry's Policy Commission on the Future of Farming and Food.

October 29

Devon FMD Inquiry publishes its preliminary findings.

November 26-27

Devon County Council's response to FMD is the subject of a presentation at the County Councils' Network meeting in Scarborough.

November 27

Government declares Devon FMD 'free' by removing its 'At Risk' status. 96% of public rights of way now open.

November 28

County Council's Development Control Committee gives DEFRA a four month deadline to close the Ash Moor Burial Pit site.

December 1

County Council presents review of impact of FMD on public rights of way network to the annual meeting of the Devon Parish Paths Partnership (P3).

APPENDIX 5

Overview of Impact of Foot and Mouth Disease

IN DEVON IN 2001 (as at October 2001)

Farms affected (peak figures)

- 173 confirmed cases (last confirmed Devon case – 17th June 2001).

- 4,500 farms under DEFRA "Form D" livestock movement restrictions (Total farms in the county - 10,500)

Livestock slaughtered

Sheep	-	282,817
Cattle	-	72,433
Pigs	-	30,845
Goats	-	108

Livestock Movement Licences issued by Devon County Council

34,000

Footpaths closed - peak figure

3,000 miles (95% of Devon's footpath network was re-opened by August 2001)

APPENDIX 6

Original Questions for DEFRA

(set out in a letter dated 27th September 2001)

1. Drawing upon the Department's experience in Devon, in other parts of the UK, and its knowledge of actions taken in Europe and elsewhere, what lessons have DEFRA learned

    *   in terms of containment of the disease;

    *   in terms of eradication of the disease?

2. Bearing in mind the immediacy of media engagement in any emergency what proposals for improving the chain of communication both within and beyond DEFRA does the Department suggest?

3. Given that farm businesses subject to form D restrictions suffered significant losses in income, were ineligible for compensation and may not access the Farm Business Advisory Service or the Business Recovery Fund, what practical and/or financial help can the Department offer or suggest?

4. What should this outbreak teach us about the future of British farming and the food production/distribution system?

5. The Secretary of State has spoken about her Department developing a Sustainable Development Strategy and agrees that reform of CAP's market support and direct payments to farmers is necessary. Is the Department able to explain how the Strategy will affect Devon businesses and how it sees the direction farming in Devon will take after CAP reform?

APPENDIX 7

The Contents of a Letter from Rt Hon Alun Michael

Dated 23 October 2001 from The Minister for Rural Affairs Rt Hon Alun Michael MP to The Chief Executive of Devon County Council

DEVON FOOT AND MOUTH INQUIRY

I am now able to reply to the questions you sent us on 27 September, in order to assist the Devon County Council Foot and Mouth Inquiry.

First, let me explain the way in which we are ensuring that the handling of the Foot and Mouth outbreak is considered fully and that all relevant lessons are learned. The Prime Minister has announced two independent inquiries. Once we are sure that FMD has been eradicated, Dr Iain Anderson will look at the lessons to be learned from the current outbreak and the way the Government should handle any future major animal disease outbreak. Separately, the Royal Society Study, chaired by Sir Brian Follett, will undertake a scientific review of questions relating to the transmission, prevention, and control of epidemic outbreaks of infectious diseases in Livestock. You can find further information from www.number-10.gov.uk .

As I indicated in my letter of 20 September, we are willing to help as much as we are able with your Inquiry, but it would not be proper for us to anticipate the findings of the national Inquiries into the Foot and Mouth outbreak. To an extent, some of the questions you have asked appear to be inviting us to do this, and I am sure you will appreciate the difficulty. In relation to question 1, we see the Devon Inquiry as providing a local perspective on the outbreak and making a contribution to the government Inquiries, as I think you do yourselves.

The "Lessons Learned" Inquiry has not yet formally begun - in order not to divert energy away from the eradication of FMD until that has been achieved - but you can forward your comments by email to andersoninquiry@cabinet-office.x.gsi.gov.uk. or send them by post to the Anderson Inquiry, Room 207, Ashley House, 2 Monck Street, London SW1P 2BQ. The Royal Society has already started its inquiry and can be contacted at The Royal Society, 6 Carlton House Terrace, London, SW1Y 5AG.

I should mention that the Policy Commission on Food and Farming will be making suggestions to Government about the long-term, and the events of the last four months are also being scrutinised by others - such as the National Audit Office, the Public Accounts Committee and the Select Committee on Agriculture - whose findings will help inform public debate.

In **question 2,** you asked what proposals we had for improving communications both within the Department and externally. Essentially there are two aspects to this. One is the Department's administrative arrangements and liaison with peerage on the ground, particularly farmers. The other is communication via the press and media, including responses to media coverage and comments from other parties.

On the first of these, we are reviewing our internal communication processes to ensure that we share knowledge more effectively. DEFRA officials have set up regular telephone conferences with our regional offices so that we can keep our staff informed of policy developments and we are reviewing our channels for internal communications so that information is properly targeted.

Regular stakeholder meetings are held by our animal health teams both nationally and locally to provide an opportunity for stakeholders to get their views across and comment on and feed into our planning. Organisations, including local government and bodies like the CLA and NFU, also work with us by using their own communication channels to convey information to their members. Stakeholder meetings also provide an invaluable opportunity for Ministers to have direct communication with the public.

It has to be recognised that there is no easy way of achieving simple and timely communications at a time of crisis, especially when the issues are complex and the future trend of the emergency - as with FMD - is difficult to predict. Those who seek answers to queries need immediate answers, while those involved in administrative, logistical or veterinary judgements have to develop - often under great pressure - decisions which will be robust in a variety of circumstances. There are practical difficulties in an emergency in keeping front line field staff sufficiently up to date with policy developments to enable them to deal with all the questions that farmers pose. We are now working to improve information flows to our staff and to equip them to pass it on to the farmers.

On the second aspect, DEFRA is continuously striving to improve public communications and to provide information that is factual and clear. Our media activity is informed by the need to disseminate information, demonstrate openness, provide clear explanations, provide accessibility to information to key personnel and to assist in the disease control effort by conveying timely and relevant messages.

Public information campaign strategy is determined by research. We follow standard procedures to produce public information material. All our campaigns are objective based with effectiveness measures built in. As I am sure you are aware, methods of communicating to date have varied from large public information campaigns on biosecurity to individual targeted mailshots, production of leaflets, videos etc.

None of these approaches is perfect. For instance, we launched a video urging stringency in biosecurity when there was worry that - for all sorts of reasons - some farmers and others might relax their vigilance. At the same time we were trying to get over the message that many restrictions on walkers were being lifted because of evidence that walkers pose minimal risk to spreading disease. It was suggested that these two approaches were inconsistent, but in fact both were based on clear veterinary and scientific advice and **both** messages were included on the video.

In **question 3** you asked about the help available to farmers under Form D restrictions. The Farm Business Advice Service (FBAS) provides free on-farm business advice to farmers and growers in England. Farmers are entitled to 3 days of consultancy advice, which provides a business health check leading to the preparation of an Action Plan that will help farmers develop better business practices and signpost them to organisations that can provide further support and advice. The FBAS is run by the Small Business Service through their Business Link network and is delivered on the ground by experienced Farm Business Advisers.

An enhanced form of the service was introduced as part of the FMD recovery package to culled out farms. However, the core service continues to run and is open to all farmers including Form D farmers. To help ease waiting lists for the service, a transfer of funds was made from the FMD enhanced service to the core service in July and ring fenced for delivery to Form D farms only.

A further budget review, due to be completed this month, aims to maximise expenditure in this financial year for both services by reviewing demand and switching funding to match requirements.

As you will appreciate, farms under Form D restrictions are not eligible for help via the Business Recovery Fund (BRF), which was set up specifically to help non-farm rural businesses, as they had no other source of help. The BRF operates using the state aids rules' exemption for de minimis grants, but currently the exemption does not extend to farming or transport.

The England Rural Development Programme and its rural economy schemes also provide a sound basis for contributing to the government's medium term objectives for rural regeneration and diversification. Over the seven-year life of the Programme, the ERDP will provide a continued and increasing source of help to projects which will contribute to the creation of more diverse and competitive agricultural and forestry sectors, new jobs, development of new products and market outlets, and provide targeted training to support these new activities. It is not, however, a good vehicle for helping with immediate short term recovery since it is constrained by limited funds and the inflexible nature of the Programme which has to meet the strict requirements of the Rural Development Regulation.

In **question 4** you asked about the lessons learned from the outbreak for the future of British farming and food production/ distribution. As indicated earlier, the Government has set up an independent Policy Commission to advise on how we create a sustainable, competitive and diverse farming and food sector within a thriving rural economy, which advances environmental, health, and animal welfare goals. Chaired by Sir Don Curry, the Commission will have a key role in informing the Government's approach to policy in the future within England.

The Policy Commission has been asked to report to the Prime Minister and Secretary of State by 31st December this year. The report will help to inform the Government's position when CAP reform proposals are published next year. Again, it would be premature for me to comment on the outcome of this study, but we would encourage your Council and anyone who has an interest in this crucial debate to send your comments to Sir Don Curry, Policy Commission on the Future of Farming and Food, Rm. LG12, Admiralty Arch, The Mall, London, SW1A 2WH or by email to farming@cabinet-office.x.gsi.gov.uk

Finally, your **fifth question** asked about sustainable development and CAP reform. The Secretary of State has announced that DEFRA will prepare its own Sustainable Development Strategy. Work on this is now under way and external stakeholders will be involved in its preparation. In November we will be publishing information on both the DEFRA and Government Sustainable Development websites seeking further comments (www.defra.gov.uk and www.sustainable-development.gov.uk). The Strategy is likely to be an overall assessment of the Department's potential contribution to sustainable development and identify particular priorities within that, rather than a comprehensive delivery plan.

I hope this is helpful. If you have further detailed questions, it would be helpful if these could be as specific and focused as possible in order to minimise the burdens for staff actively engaged in disease control operations.

I have replied to this correspondence myself because of our earlier useful contacts over the inquiry. From now on responsibility within the Department for co-ordinating evidence to inquiries will rest with my colleague Lord Whitty, to whom all future correspondence should be addressed.

We look forward to hearing about the findings of the Devon County Council Inquiry.

APPENDIX 8

DEFRA's Response to Supplementary Questions
(December 2001)

DEFRA

Department for
Environment,
Food & Rural Affairs

Nobel House
17 Smith Square
London SW1P 3JR

Tel: 020 7238/5387/5790/5385/5386
Fax: 020 7238 1100
email: pus.lords@defra.gsi.gov.uk

Mr Brian Wilkinson
FMD Inquiry Co-ordinator
Devon County Council
County Hall
Topsham Road
Exeter
Devon
EX2 4QD

20 December 2001

THE DEVON FOOT AND MOUTH INQUIRY

Thank you for your letter of 9 November passing on some further questions from the Chairman of Devon FMD Inquiry, Professor Mercer.

Several of these seek our views on general issues that have arisen from the recent outbreak or on future action that we might take. However, we expect that these matters will be considered by the two national Inquiries that have been established by the Government and to which Alun Michael referred in his letter of 23 October to your Chief Executive, Philip Jenkinson. While I am happy to reply fully to those questions that relate specifically to the present outbreak, I do not think that it would be right to pre-empt the results of the Inquiries.

The attached replies therefore answer Professor Mercer's questions as far as possible but not where we expect the matter to be considered by the national Inquiries and where it would therefore be premature to reply until we have received their reports. Questions 2, 10 (as regards future policy), 11 and 12 fall into this category. The Inquiry reports are also likely to influence our future actions in respect of other issues such as communications and again reference is made to this in the relevant replies.

Finally, I am also attaching some material that we have prepared for the use of local authority inquiries. This is intended to provide some general information on various topics, which the Inquiry may wish to take into account. The information given is correct to the best of our knowledge and belief but it is not, and is not intended to be, a comprehensive account of what happened during the outbreak. Nor does it seek to draw any conclusions about the future, for which we await the reports of the national Inquiries It is simply intended to be of assistance to your Inquiry although I appreciate that the Devon team may have already covered a lot of this ground.

The information should predominantly already be in the public domain although it has been grouped together here for convenience under the following headings:

- Contingency planning (including the role of the army)
- Slaughter policy
- Vaccination
- Communications/openness
- Local discretion
- Scientific advice on FMD
- Source of the outbreak
- Disposal issues
- Biosecurity
- Welfare of animals
- Compensation for the compulsory slaughter of livestock
- Cleansing and disinfection of premises
- Import controls
- Impact on agriculture
- Movement of animals
- Impact on the rural economy
- Access to the countryside

LORD WHITTY

(approved by the Minister and signed in his absence)

ANNEX TO LORD WHITTY'S LETTER

REPLIES TO QUESTIONS FROM THE DEVON COUNTY COUNCIL FMD INQUIRY

Q1.   Can we see FMD contingency plan to which MAFF (DEFRA) were working during the current crisis to aid decision-making?

A.   The FMD Contingency Plan can be found on the DEFRA website (http://www.defra.gov.uk/animalh/diseases/control/contingency/index.htm); a hard copy is attached. Risk simulation exercises were frequently carried out (84 between 1995 - 1999).

Q2.   *What precisely is being done to develop a new multi-agency national contingency plan to apply in the event of any future outbreak. How is it proposed to rehearse the plan regularly with the other agencies involved, including local authorities?*

A.   Contingency planning is being reviewed against the possibility of further cases of disease arising. However, in the longer term contingency planning is a matter that we expect to be considered by the national Inquiries and it would therefore be premature to reply fully until we have received their reports.

Q3.   *DEFRA is seeking to improve communications to farmers via local office staff. Many who submitted to our Inquiry considered that this was a weakness during the current crisis. Will improvements include the setting up of an integrated emergency call centre staffed by adequate numbers of experienced and well-informed personnel able to give farmers accurate, up-to-date and unambiguous information from the outset?*

A.   We have started to address this in the following ways:

• Communications Directorate in DEFRA is developing wide ranging contingency plans to deal with emergency situations such as further FMD outbreaks. Part of these plans could include rapidly putting in place emergency call centres, and having communications channels in place to ensure they have all relevant information.

• We are currently engaged in a quantitative research exercise to determine how best to communicate with the farming community. This will provide us with valuable information on how best to involve staff at a local level.

We will also be studying carefully the outcome of the national inquiries.

Q4.   *You mention stakeholder meetings in your response to our first questions; will County Councils be invited to them?*

A.   The Trading Standards Department of Devon County Council attended the weekly FMD stakeholders meeting in Devon. However, communications with stakeholders is likely to be a matter that is considered by the national Inquiries and we shall need to study carefully the outcome of the national inquiries.

Q5.   *Communications with media were not seen by those involved at the local level to be adequate to meet the demands required. While you say in your response that 'you are continuously striving to improve public communications', attendance at news briefings and copies of your daily information sheet were not available to some information spreading organisations such as the County Council. Will this be improved in any future outbreak or emergency and what are your proposals to ensure any future contingency plan contains an effective communications plan, which will spell out the process and accountabilities?*

A.   At local level we issued daily bulletins and summaries. In sending out these we always consulted with the local authority, in particular trading standards and animal health and environmental services.

Devon County Council press officers were invited to every press conference. They always received advance copies of Press Releases, newsletters and were welcome to attend at any time. Indeed, some press conferences featured county council figures such as a trading standards or environmental health official.

Devon County Council often called their own press conferences and we were invited.

Whenever we could and whenever asked we always shared what information we had.

There are lessons to be learned, and we are already putting steps in place to improve communications. At local level we will be meeting councils and other services see how we can improve emergency communications for the future.

We will also be studying carefully the outcome of the national inquiries on this matter.

Q6. *What steps are being taken to improve the Department and Government's database of local government contacts? The LGA's report on the 2001 outbreak highlighted the disappointing communications between local government and the then MAFF and the fact that central Government did not appear to have the necessary database to e-mail local authority chief executives directly.*

A.   Communications with local authorities are very important for DEFRA. Communications to all local authorities are sent via the relevant local authority association, e.g. the LGA and LACOTS, which have clear lines of communications with all their member authorities. We will also be studying carefully the outcome of the national inquiries on communications with local authorities.

Q7. *In his report "Rural Recovery after Foot and Mouth Disease", Lord Haskins makes the point that those farmers who have not lost their stock, but are unable to move them for sale or to other grassland, have probably suffered more economically than those farmers whose livestock were slaughtered. He recommends "special compensation" for these farmers. It is clear from his report that he means over-and-above action already taken by Government. He also warns of the serious welfare problems that arise with these "locked up" herds when the grass runs out. Up to 4,500 Devon farmers have been in this situation. What action is the Government taking to provide retrospective financial support to help these farms recover? What action is being taken to assist farms still in this situation and avert animal welfare problems?*

A.   Alun Michael recently responded formally to Lord Haskins' report (in England's Rural Future) and a copy is enclosed herewith. It is not Government policy to provide compensation for consequential losses arising from the FMD outbreak. As regards the impact on animal welfare of movement restrictions, the key here is to lift the restrictions as soon as is practicable and considerable progress has been made, for instance by Devon becoming a free county on 27 November. Where restrictions still apply and the provision of fodder is a problem, some charities offer assistance. For example, the Arthur Rank Centre's Addington Fund has a National Fodder Bureau to broker the supply of fodder and to assist those in financial need with the cost as well as the associated haulage costs. The Government is providing support to such charities in the form of match funding, and recently announced an extension of the match-funding scheme to run from September to the end of the year. Finally, where welfare problems cannot be resolved, the Livestock Welfare Disposal Scheme provides a further option.

Q8. *Why did the then Ministry commence work on the Ash Moor project (reportedly costing £7million) without undertaking an Environmental Impact Assessment or prior consultation with the County Council? What plans are there for the future of the Ash Moor burial site? If it is to be used for its original purpose, will it be a national resource or a purely local one? And if it is to be a national asset will you be submitting an entirely fresh NOPD (Notification of Proposed Development) as is required in those circumstances?*

A.   Work was commenced on the preparation of the Ash Moor mass burial site in Devon in response to the intense local need to dispose of animal carcasses during the height of the Foot and Mouth outbreak. The disease had significantly affected Devon and preferred means of disposal of carcasses were predicted to be insufficient.

On 30 March DEFRA's Exeter Office set out the factors leading to the decision to use Ash Moor as a burial site. The Environment Agency carried out an initial risk assessment of the site on 11 April. Construction of the first cell commenced on 20 April. On 24 April 2001 a letter from Devon County Council to the then MAFF conveyed consent for the development of the site under Circular 18/84: 'Crown Land and Crown Development.

Halcrow Group Limited have carried out retrospectively a detailed Environmental Impact Assessment on behalf of DEFRA as sponsors of the project. The Assessment was carried out during August and September 2001 and the draft report is currently subject to consultation.

On 14 May 2001, in the light of the incidence of the disease, DEFRA instructed that work should cease on the Ash Moor site. The site was effectively mothballed and has remained in its present state of maintenance against possible future operational use. To date no carcasses have been disposed of at the site and there are no current plans to use the Ash Moor site for the disposal of animal carcasses.

The present position with regard to the Ash Moor site as with other sites, is that it has been mothballed until there is a firm and agreed policy on procedures to deal with recrudescence or any new outbreak of disease. DEFRA officials will be meeting Devon County Council in the New Year to discuss the future of the site.

Q9. The Inquiry heard evidence that a family living adjacent to the Ash Moor burial pit was given less than 24 hours notice before work was due to start and then advised by an MoD official to move. Does the Department accept that the way the news was broken to the family concerned was badly handled and what steps would it now take to ensure more sensitive consultation? Is the Department prepared to apologise to the family for the way they were treated? This would go a long way in addressing the emotional burden placed on and still being felt by this family.

A.   Although it would not be appropriate to comment on an individual case, DEFRA regrets any distress that may have been caused to the family concerned.

Q10. Does the Minister now consider, in the light of experience, that vaccination as a means of 'ring-fencing' an outbreak, could reduce the number of livestock culled, or at least reconcile the rate of slaughter with the rate of disposal?

A.   There has never been a disagreement that ring-vaccination could be a useful disease control measure providing the right circumstances prevail. Ring vaccination was not a practical measure at the start of our outbreak since it was soon clear that the virus had potentially been spread across a wide area and many animals. According to some independent studies using ring vaccination at that time could have made the situation worse if this had been the principal control mechanism.

Q11. Given that vaccination is used routinely in this country to tackle other livestock diseases and that the meat from such livestock is subsequently sold by supermarkets without comment, would the Department agree that there is no justifiable reason in commercial terms why Foot and Mouth vaccinated livestock could not be treated in the same way?

A.   This is not strictly a like for like comparison. Again, the EU single market has implications for any consideration of a change of policy. This is why the UK was co-organiser of an international conference on FMD, which was held in Brussels on 12/13 December. One of the strong messages emerging from that conference was the urgent need for international verification of a test which can distinguish between vaccinated and unvaccinated animals. This is also a matter that we expect to be considered by the national Inquiries. It would therefore be premature to come to a conclusion until we have received their reports but it would be wrong to suggest the food industry do not have concerns about a foot and mouth vaccination policy. Some of this concern stems from the fact that under EU rules products from animals vaccinated against foot and mouth disease would have to be handled and treated separately to products from animals that have not been so vaccinated.

A. It should be noted that the policy was not applied indiscriminately or without consideration of local conditions, as this question implies. The contiguous premises cull was an approach based on a general scientific and veterinary judgement, with provision for proportionate exceptions at local level based on local veterinary judgement.

The contiguous premises policy when introduced in late March was based on veterinary and epidemiological advice given to DEFRA by its experts, that in all the circumstances of this FMD outbreak animals on premises contiguous to IPs were exposed to disease. However, where a farmer asserted that his animals had not been exposed, a re-assessment was performed by local vets to determine whether or not there were any factors which demonstrated that exposure had not in fact occurred. If for any of a number of reasons exposed cattle or pigs on a CP had not been culled within 21 days of the confirmation of disease on the relevant IP, those animals on that CP were exempted from slaughter if they showed no clinical signs of disease.

The CP slaughter policy was further refined at the end of April, by extending the scope for local veterinary judgement:-

• Cattle could be spared if there was adequate biosecurity (but not if they had grazed within 50 metres of an IP boundary since 1 February).

• A strictly limited exemption for rare breed sheep, was introduced if they could be isolated from other stock and strict biosecurity was imposed.

The previous exemption for cattle and pigs if no clinical signs had appeared for 21 days after the relevant IP was retained.

Independent studies have demonstrated that without the culling policy adopted, the outbreak would have been far worse and, indeed, cases could still be occurring now. Practical experience of controlling the disease outbreak in the Brecon Beacons demonstrated that disease was not brought under control until contiguous culling was implemented.

In the longer term, this is a matter that we expect to be considered by the national Inquiries and we will wish to take account of their reports.

A. DEFRA field epidemiologists have completed the review of the infected premises in the area around Knowstone. This is to ensure that epidemiological links between IPs have not been missed and to collate the epidemiological information for defined clusters.

Having done this there is only one IP in Witheridge, which is about 8km south of Knowstone, which has a theoretical epidemiological link to a funeral pyre on the basis of its proximity and timing, in terms of the date of the pyre and the estimated date the IP became infected. There was no evidence of debris from the pyre merely the above link and the farm could have been infected by other means.

The Meteorological Office has used information on the location and dates of some of the pyres in Devon for an analysis of possible airborne spread. This has not revealed any evidence that pyres had resulted in infection downwind of these pyres.

DEFRA is responsible for such disposal operations which are carried out in such a way so as to prevent any further spread of disease from unburnt animal tissue.

Q14. The widely publicised images of burning pyres and the associated concerns about public health did great damage to Devon's national and international tourism business. Does the Ministry agree that in future pyres should be used only as a last resort and in any case, be of single small farm scale?

A. At the beginning of the outbreak, disposal took account of the Northumberland report, which recommended burial or, where this was not possible, burning on a pyre. On strictly veterinary grounds it is more appropriate to destroy and dispose of carcasses on farm rather than taking potentially contaminated material off the farm. However, agreement was subsequently reached between DEFRA and the various interested Government Departments and agencies on 24 April on a hierarchy of disposal. This is as follows:

	Type of animals
Rendering	All (essential for cattle born before 1 August 1996)
Incineration	All
Landfill	Cattle born after 1 August 1996, sheep and pigs
Burn	All
Bury	Cattle born after August 1996, sheep and pigs

In terms of disposal policy in future outbreaks, this is a matter that we expect to be considered by the national Inquiries and we will need to study carefully the outcome on this matter.

Q15. The Inquiry also heard evidence from Knowstone Parish Council that the culling operation at the village was bungled, a herd of cows was shot on the run and that it took several days to complete the slaughter. The Parish Council expressed dismay that the Ministry did not act within the law and used an excessive Police support to enforce its decisions. Does the Department accept the Parish Council's criticisms and does the Department agree that the insensitive handling of this cull did nothing to foster a united front against Foot and Mouth? Has the Department conducted an investigation into the conduct of the Knowstone cull either wholly or in partnership with other agencies? What steps has the Department undertaken to ensure that all future culls are conducted efficiently and with sensitivity?

A. DEFRA very much regrets the conduct of this particular cull. Cattle handling facilities were limited and twenty-four yearling Limousins, which were not used to humans, managed to escape. Re-gathering them would have been likely to result in the animals running further away from the farm potentially spreading disease over a wide area. The decision was therefore made to cull them using marksmen. Regrettably the marksman selected was only able to cull 6 and only succeeded in dispersing the remaining animals further. An expert stalker eventually completed the task. New instructions have been issued nationally to ensure that sufficiently skilled marksmen are selected in future.

Q16. To assist in the recovery and revival of the Devon economy it would help if Government spending on tourism promotion in England matched that for Scotland and Wales. Will the Ministry press for this level playing field and in particular repeat and reinforce the Department of Culture Media and Sport Select Committee recommendation that "It will be essential to promote areas most adversely affected by the current crisis with public funding"?

A.   The Department for Culture Media and Sport published the Government response to the fourth report from the Culture, Media and Sport Select Committee, Commons Session 2000-2001 on 17 October 2001 (Cmnd 5279). A detailed response to the issue raised can be found at pages 4-6 of the document.

Q17. Will there be funding for the voluntary and religious psychological support when they are deployed during crisis times?

A.   Although the Government cannot commit to open ended funding of these sectors, it can play a significant role in promoting voluntary and community activity in all parts of society. This commitment is clearly set out in the Compact between Government and the voluntary and community sector in England.

The Government recognises the important role that the voluntary and religious sector plays in supporting rural communities during times of crisis. The Department for Environment, Food and Rural Affairs and the Department of Health are working closely in partnership with these sectors through the Rural Stress Action Plan (RSAP). DEFRA has in total made available close to £1 million to the RSAP group as well as providing temporary accommodation. This valuable partnership forms part of an essential support network for those in distress in rural areas. We hope to continue building on this good working relationship.

The Government has also funded the Rural Stress Information Network (RSIN) to establish a network of support available to people in rural communities who are suffering from stress. The network includes professional health care staff and voluntary organisations with relevant expertise (Samaritans, MIND etc) together with legal, financial and business support.

The Government is also providing support to such charities the Arthur Rank Centre's Addington Fund in the form of match funding, and recently announced an extension of the match-funding scheme to run from September to the end of the year. The Fund gives support to farmers in need who have increased costs due to FMD. In addition to this, the Addington Fund now also provides one-off support payments to non-agricultural rural businesses where FMD has an impact.

DEFRA COMMENTS TO INQUIRIES ON FOOT-AND-MOUTH DISEASE (FMD): CONTINGENCY PLANNING

- Before the outbreak there was a contingency plan for FMD (and other animal diseases). A Great Britain contingency plan was submitted to the EU in 1993 and has been up-dated as necessary since then. However, it is accepted that this contingency plan was largely internal - essentially for officials and vets. In addition, eighty-four risk simulation exercises were carried out between 1995 - 1999.

- It has to be recognised that the size and scale of the outbreak was unprecedented. Accordingly the outbreak exceeded the ability of the resources available under the contingency plans to deal with it effectively.

Steps were taken as follows:

- Rapid steps were taken to recruit non-SVS vets in the UK and abroad. At the end of the first week of the outbreak (25 February), 421 veterinary staff were deployed. This rose to a peak of about 1800 in mid-May.

- On the day that the first case was confirmed (20 February), the office of the Minister of State (Lords) in MAFF contacted the office of the Minister for the Armed Forces to warn of the possibility of future requests for military assistance.

- On 14 March, a Director of Operations was appointed in London. On 19 March Regional Operations Directors were appointed for Cumbria and Devon (and at later dates to other centres).

- Around 20 March, ADAS, an organisation with close associations with livestock farmers, were recruited to provide additional support to undertake the proposed vaccination programme for North Cumbria and possibly Devon had that gone ahead. Commercial supplies of the relevant vaccine have also been built up as a precautionary measure.

- On 14 March, military vets were deployed to support MAFF. On 15 March, a military logistics team was deployed to the MAFF Headquarters in London. On 19 March, the military was deployed in Devon and the next day in Cumbria (and other regions thereafter).

- On 26 March, a Joint Co-ordination Centre was established in London jointly by the army and MAFF. Local army Headquarters were established in Exeter, Worcester, Carlisle and Dumfries with military liaison officers appointed to other Regions. The role of these Headquarters was to co-ordinate logistics and other support to MAFF and then DEFRA, drawn from appropriate civil and military resources. Teams of armed forces personnel also helped to co-ordinate the administration of slaughter and the transport and disposal of carcasses in affected areas. The armed forces contribution to the operation was directed by Land Command under Commander-in-Chief Land. Over 2000 forces personnel were deployed by 15 April but thereafter the number reduced. However, the army remained available for deployment (as in the Hexham outbreak after 24 August).

- Currently DEFRA is fully ready and equipped to deal with any new FMD cases, should any further cases arise in the current outbreak.

- For the future, a revised contingency plan will be more inclusive, building on the newly forged links between DEFRA and its stakeholders at both national and local level and will be informed by the outcome of the Lessons Learned inquiry.

DEFRA COMMENTS TO INQUIRIES ON FOOT-AND-MOUTH DISEASE (FMD): SLAUGHTER POLICY

Government priority has been to eradicate FMD as quickly as possible.

To achieve this, the policy is as follows:

- Cull all susceptible animals on confirmed infected farms within 24 hours of the first report of the disease by the farmer.

- Cull all susceptible livestock on farms neighbouring an infected farm (contiguous premises) within 48 hours of the first report other than in the cases described below. It is necessary to cull animals exposed to disease even if they are not showing signs of disease. By the time signs develop the animals would have been breathing out the virus for several days, and dairy cows will have been excreting virus in their milk, running a high risk of spreading the disease further.

- Cull all animals on farms that are considered to be dangerous contacts i.e. where there is a close link to a confirmed case due to for example movement of animals, people, vehicles or equipment.

- Slaughter on suspicion animals that can not be clinically diagnosed but which are suspected on veterinary grounds to be infected. In these cases a full set of diagnostic samples as well as a statistical bleed of any sheep present is taken. Contiguous premises are not immediately culled. If the laboratory results confirm the disease the case becomes confirmed and the contiguous premises are culled.

This policy has applied since the first case of disease (although the contiguous premises policy was not introduced until the end of March). In addition, the Minister announced on 15 March that pigs and sheep within 3 km of infected premises in Cumbria and Dumfries and Galloway would also be subject to culling on the grounds that they had been exposed to infection. The cull was completed in Dumfries and Galloway and replaced by serological testing in Cumbria on 24 May.

The contiguous premises policy when introduced in late March was based on veterinary and epidemiological advice given to DEFRA by its experts, that in all the circumstances of this FMD outbreak animals on premises contiguous to IPs were exposed to disease. However where a farmer asserted that his animals had not been exposed, a re-assessment was performed by local vets to determine whether or not there were any factors which demonstrated that exposure had not in fact occurred. If for any of a number of reasons (e.g. farmer resistance) exposed cattle or pigs on a CP had not been culled within 21 days of the confirmation of disease on the relevant IP, those animals on that CP were exempted from slaughter if they showed no clinical signs of disease.

The contiguous premises slaughter policy was further refined at the end of April, by extending the scope for local veterinary judgement: -

- Cattle could be spared if there was adequate biosecurity (but not if they had grazed within 50 metres of an IP boundary since 1 February).

- A strictly limited exemption for rare breed and hefted sheep, was introduced if they could be isolated from other stock and strict biosecurity was imposed.

The previous exemption for cattle and pigs if no clinical signs had appeared for 21 days after the relevant IP was **retained**. In July, an exemption policy for rare breeds of pigs and for small camelids was introduced providing strict biosecurity measures were met.

In terms of the overall slaughter policy, it should be noted that:

- Scientific advice is that the policy of culling susceptible animals on contiguous farms was vital to get ahead of the infection by removing animals that were already potentially incubating the FMD virus. This advice was informed by four different epidemiological models.

- However, it was not always possible to meet the target of slaughtering susceptible animals on contiguous premises within 48 hours of the first report. Sometimes this was due to lack of resources in a particular area, or physical access difficulties. Some delays also due to farmer resistance or legal challenge. Epidemiological data suggests that such delays did extend the outbreak. The proposed Animal Health (Amendment) Bill will lessen delays due to inappropriate action by farmers.

- All farmers are paid full market value as compensation for any animals slaughtered as a result of the FMD outbreak.

- Everyone engaged in the slaughter and killing process must have the knowledge and skill necessary to perform the tasks humanely and efficiently in accordance with Schedule 1 of the Welfare of Animals (Slaughter or Killing) Regulations 1995. Where members of the armed forces were involved in the foot and mouth cull they were trained beforehand. Outside slaughterhouses, Veterinary Officers of the State Veterinary Service enforce the legislation.

DEFRA COMMENTS TO INQUIRIES ON FOOT-AND-MOUTH DISEASE (FMD): VACCINATION

- The Government's primary objective has been to eradicate Foot and Mouth Disease.

- Vaccination would be used if it were clear that it was the most appropriate measure to shorten the outbreak.

- **Where vaccination is used we would want to ensure that disease would not continue to circulate. Vaccination does not provide complete protection and can mask infection.**

It should be noted that:

- Contingency plans for emergency vaccination existed prior to the outbreak. They reflected requirements of European legislation (Council Directive 85/511) that vaccination against FMD has been prohibited since 1992. Emergency vaccination is permitted when an outbreak threatens to become extensive subject to the vaccination plans being submitted for scrutiny and approval by the European Commission and other Member States.

- European rules for emergency vaccination also cover requirements to (i) prohibit the movement of vaccinated animals from the vaccination zone for a period of at least 12 months (unless the animals are to be culled); (ii) keep products from vaccinated animals separate from products from non-vaccinated animals until heat or other prescribed treatments have been undertaken; and (iii) prescribe the treatments

- Throughout the outbreak, the Government have kept vaccination actively under review. Vaccination would be used if scientific advice were clear that it was the most appropriate measure to shorten the outbreak. But vaccination on its own could never have eradicated FMD entirely.

- Ring vaccination can be used with or without culling around an infected farm or area. However, the ring would have to be very large to catch all secondary cases, some of which have appeared in this outbreak more than 10 km from the source. This strategy was not used at the start of the outbreak because it was too late by the time FMD was identified in the UK. A large number of movements had taken place before the first case of FMD was identified and therefore the virus had potentially been spread across a very wide area, making ring vaccination impractical. Furthermore, however much care is taken, ring vaccination may not be completely effective in containing infection within an infected area.

- Ring vaccination was considered for clusters of new cases that occurred later in the outbreak, e.g. Hexham. In these cases the Chief Scientific Adviser and Chief Veterinary Officer advised that tighter biosecurity measures and culling would be the most effective and fastest measures to eradicate the disease in those areas.

- Pre-emptive vaccination of pigs was also considered when the Thirsk cluster of cases posed a renewed threat to the major pig production areas of the country. The risk and cost/benefit analysis did not support the case for vaccination, not least because of the post-vaccination requirements to de-bone and mature meat (<pH 6) which is difficult to achieve for pork.

- **The Government's scientific and veterinary advisers have recommended limited use of vaccination only once during this outbreak. It was clear that the vaccination plan for cattle in part of Cumbria did not have local support (from farmers, retailers and consumers). Without co-operation from farmers, it would not have been possible to implement quickly enough to be effective. There was only a very limited window of opportunity when vaccination was an option - i.e. before cattle were turned out.**

- Vaccination of rare breeds was considered by scientific and veterinary advisers at the appropriate time but was not recommended. Other measures to protect rare breeds of sheep were announced on 26 April and, in July, for rare breeds of pigs and for small camelids.

- **Current scientific and veterinary advice is that vaccination would not help in the present disease situation.**

- The use of vaccination in the Netherlands earlier this year did not save animals' lives. In fact for each case more animals were killed than would have been under the UK's contiguous cull policy (10,000 animals per case in the Netherlands compared to 2000 per case in the UK). All vaccinated animals were killed and destroyed as required by the EU Decision that permitted the Dutch vaccination programme.

- The Government recognised early in the outbreak that future EU and international policies for handling FMD would need to be reassessed, including the role of vaccination. The UK, with the Dutch, took the initiative to organise a conference that takes place in December 2001. Topics will include the possible future use of vaccination.

- All livestock farmers were sent a leaflet in April about vaccination, including the Government's responses to over 50 questions posed by the NFU. Information about the use of vaccination has also been placed on the DEFRA FMD website and kept up to date (www.defra.gsi.gov.uk/footandmouth/vaccination).

DEFRA COMMENTS TO INQUIRIES ON FOOT-AND-MOUTH DISEASE (FMD): COMMUNICATIONS/OPENNESS

Means of communication used were as follows:

- A dedicated FMD website updated continuously during the day, providing news, advice and facts relating to the disease and farm operations as affected by the disease

- Regular press conferences and specialist press briefings

- Regular stakeholder meetings at HQ (in London) and at regional level

- Telephone helplines (general DEFRA helpline, FMD helpline, animal movements helpline, LACOTS helpline, local office numbers)

- Letters to farmers on: biosecurity (March, 2 in April, May, July), vaccination (April) and autumn movements (letters from Lord Whitty to farmers and to LACOTS).

- Leaflets on FMD.

- A video on biosecurity sent to all farmers in July.

- Regional communications e.g. Devon newsletter.

- FMD update sent to farmers in August.

- Central media briefing (by NCC and latterly DEFRA Briefing Unit)

- Advice on access to the countryside.

Communications were made as open as possible. In particular:

- The website includes a full list of Infected Places where FMD has been confirmed. Disclosure of this information is deemed to be necessary for the purposes of disease control and therefore in the public interest and allowed under the Data Protection Act.

- A set of veterinary risk assessments, which underlie FMD control policies being applied, has been placed in the public domain.

- Emerging policies have been discussed wherever possible with the stakeholder community.

DEFRA COMMENTS TO INQUIRIES ON FOOT-AND-MOUTH DISEASE (FMD): LOCAL DISCRETION

Diagnosis of disease

- It is standard practice in a disease-free country to confirm foot and mouth disease using laboratory tests and this is required by Council Directive 85/511/EEC.

- The animals in the first outbreak reported were put under movement restrictions immediately on suspicion of infection, and the Institute for Animal Health (IAH) at Pirbright confirmed the diagnosis the following day. The IAH carried out an ELISA test; which takes about five to six hours to complete.

- As the outbreak progressed, DEFRA moved quickly to a position whereby a greater proportion of cases were diagnosed on clinical signs. The policy is now to slaughter immediately on clinical diagnosis or suspicion of disease.

- If the vet on the farm makes a clear clinical diagnosis of FMD and has evidence to support it, then disease will be confirmed. The case is then included in the day's confirmed new cases figure.

- The normal practice is that the clinical diagnosis is phoned through to Head Office in London and authorisation to slaughter stock is then given during the same telephone call. However, the SVS were advised on 27 March 2001 that the inspecting veterinary surgeon could authorise slaughter immediately to ensure the slaughter process was not delayed if any problem in communicating with Head Office occurred.

Disease control

- EU Council Directive 85/511/EEC introducing Community measures for the control of FMD lays down obligatory procedures in terms of reporting and controlling disease (a draft Directive is due to come forward for discussion in the EU Council of Ministers which will take account of the new and changing situation since the original Directive was produced in the 1980s).

- Subject to the EU requirements, policy for disease control is set nationally on the best overall veterinary and scientific advice. It is important to ensure that policy is applied rigorously in all areas.

- Disease control is the responsibility of local Disease Control Centres.

- Local discretion is exercised wherever necessary, e.g. in decisions on slaughter on contiguous premises.

- Local pilot exercises have been carried out, e.g. a study to help farmers assess and deal with the risk of turning out cattle to pasture from their winter quarters took place in parts of Staffordshire, Cheshire, and Derbyshire. The results from the exercise were be used to arrive at an assessment of the risks of spread of disease from turning out cattle or from movement of sheep in specific areas.

Operations

- The FMD contingency plan assumed that operations would be carried out regionally under central guidelines.

- Senior officials were appointed to be Regional Operations Directors from 19 March. They were responsible for liasing with local stakeholders.

- The Joint Co-ordination Centre in London acts as focus for Regional Operations Directors receives regular reports and disseminates information and guidance nationally.

DEFRA COMMENTS TO INQUIRIES ON FOOT-AND-MOUTH DISEASE (FMD): SCIENTIFIC ADVICE

- The Chief Scientific Adviser (CSA), Professor David King, is responsible to the Prime Minister and members of the UK Cabinet for ensuring that the Government has access to the best possible scientific advice on which to base its policy decisions.

- On 24 March the Prime Minister asked the CSA to establish a group of scientific experts to advise on the FMD epidemic.

- The FMD science group was not set up to be a consensus forming body. It was constitute so as to include a range of views on the scientific aspects of tackling the outbreak. Its purpose is to help the CSA decide on and formulate advice to Government by means of discussion and debate.

- The core of the group was formed of four teams of epidemiologists. Three from universities (Imperial College, Cambridge and Edinburgh) and the MAFF/Veterinary Laboratories Agency team.

- Veterinary practitioners, animal health experts, logisticians and other disciplines also participated in the work of the group which met daily for the first few weeks and has now held over thirty meetings.

- The four independent epidemiological models provided a means of exploring alternative strategies (including the use of vaccination) for bringing the epidemic under control. These showed that speeding up the culling of animals on infected premises (to 24 hrs) and culling of animals on contiguous premises (within 48 hrs) was the best option.

- The group has considered a number of other scientific issues including vaccination, diagnostic testing and biosecurity.

- Many of those who participated in the work of the group have published papers on the science of the epidemic in peer reviewed journals. In addition, the CSA has given numerous media briefings and has written an article (published in the Daily Telegraph of 21 September) on the scientific issues relating to FMD vaccination.

DEFRA COMMENTS TO INQUIRIES ON FOOT-AND-MOUTH DISEASE (FMD): SOURCE OF THE OUTBREAK

- A great deal of epidemiological research has been conducted into the origins of this outbreak.

- The current epidemic has been caused by a specific strain of the foot and mouth virus (PanAsian Strain O) which has occurred in a number of countries around the world.

- The precise means of introduction of the virus is unknown and subject to continuing investigations. It may have been introduced in illegally imported meat or meat products. It would not be appropriate to comment further on the specific question of the source or sources of the outbreak until all investigations are complete.

- **The earliest case of FMD identified to date occurred at a holding in Heddon-on-the-Wall (case number 2001/04). Pigs from this holding were sent to an abattoir in Essex where the first identified case of FMD was confirmed on 20 February.**

- **During the period of infectivity before FMD was confirmed on IP FMD 2001/04, windborne spread of virus had infected cattle and sheep on nearby farms in Northumberland.**

- Subsequent spread of the disease was mainly through movement of animals, particularly sheep.

DEFRA COMMENTS TO INQUIRIES ON FOOT-AND-MOUTH DISEASE (FMD): DISPOSAL ISSUES

- Nearly 4 million animals have been destroyed in the current outbreak for disease control purposes. This has presented a major problem in respect of disposal both in terms of logistics, particularly when very large numbers of animals were being killed at the height of the outbreak, and the means of disposal.

- At the outset, disposal took account of the Northumberland report, which recommended burial or, where this was not possible, burning on a pyre. On strictly veterinary grounds it is more appropriate to destroy and dispose of carcasses on farm rather than taking potentially contaminated material off the farm. The contingency plan was therefore based on on-farm disposal routes.

- Agreement was subsequently reached between DEFRA and the various interested Government Departments and agencies on 24 April on a hierarchy of disposal. This is as follows:

	Type of animals
Rendering	All (essential for cattle born before 1 August 1996)
Incineration	All
Landfill	Cattle born after 1 August 1996, sheep and pigs
Burn	All
Bury	Cattle born after August 1996, sheep and pigs

- **Rendering, the preferred disposal route, was used from an early date. However, this required adequate biosecurity arrangements to be put in place at the rendering plants to ensure that virus would not be spread by water or air borne routes. It was also necessary to ensure that the lorries carrying carcasses to rendering were leak proof (checked by using dye to ensure that there was no leakage from lorries). After the protocols for loading lorries and leak testing certification as well as operational procedures for rendering plants and emergency procedures during transport had been put in place, the first rendering plant dedicated to FMD disposal came on stream on 9 March with further capacity added as it became available.). Due to the overall shortfall of rendering capacity, and the need to retain some rendering capacity for dealing with slaughterhouse wastes, other means of disposal were used widely in the earlier stages of the outbreak. However, rendering was usually the sole means of disposal when the daily number of confirmed cases dropped to 5 or below (which became the general rule from mid-June).**

- However, given the need to urgently dispose of large numbers of carcasses, the other means of disposal were heavily used.

- **Where carcasses have been burnt, wherever possible ash from the pyres is being buried on site but in some cases ground conditions rule this option out. Ash that cannot be buried is being transported to Calvert and a number of**

other landfill sites. These sites are all well engineered facilities that have been purpose-designed to minimise any risks to the environment and human health. Sites are subject to site specific risk assessments and continuous monitoring.

- The Food Standards Agency is conducting a study into dioxins and dioxin-like polychlorinated biphenyls in foods from farms close to pyres. To date, three reports on this study have been published. In the latest report, the Agency considers that the available results show that pyres have posed no additional risk to health through the food supply and, although a few results remain to be reported, they do not expect them to change the situation.

- Burial on farms was also used where the Environment Agency gave the necessary approvals, i.e. groundwater authorisations following site specific risk assessments.

- **Mass burial sites were created in certain locations to cope with the needs. Such sites were established and used at Birkshaw Forest, Lockerbie; Great Orton, Cumbria; Throckmorton, Worcestershire; and Tow Law, Durham. These sites are not being used at present. A further site at Widdrington, Northumberland was used and is now closed and a site was prepared at Ash Moor, Devon but there are no current plans to use it.**

- **Mass burial sites were last used for three days at the beginning of September and previously not since 11 July.**

- **Movements of carcasses to sites other than the farm of origin for disposal were carried out in accordance with a published veterinary risk assessment.**

- **A further 2.5 million animals have been killed mainly in abattoirs under the Livestock Welfare Disposal Scheme. These have been disposed of by rendering or to licensed landfill.**

DEFRA COMMENTS TO INQUIRIES ON FOOT-AND-MOUTH DISEASE (FMD): BIOSECURITY

- The Government's top priority is to beat the disease. To this end, tight biosecurity is essential: especially by farmers and others who work in close contact with animals and are far more likely than others to have been in contact with FMD without knowing it.

- There is no room for complacency. Everyone must play their part in the fight against FMD.

- Advice on biosecurity has been has provided to all those involved since the first outbreak of the disease. MAFF/DEFRA sent Factsheets to all livestock farmers in March, April and May. Advice was also provided to hauliers, and to the general public visiting the countryside.

- The importance of good biosecurity was emphasised by the production of a video on biosecurity in July. This was sent to all livestock farmers and could also be seen on the DEFRA website. Areas with significant disease targeted with visits from ministers, senior vets and representatives from the Chief Scientists Group. Publicity campaign includes advertisements in farming and local press, targeting particularly areas, which may be at risk of FMD spread.

- Hotspots of disease in North Yorkshire, Cumbria and Northumberland have been contained by imposing Restricted Infected Area - "blue box" restrictions - a tight clampdown on the biosecurity of premises and vehicles around a designated area together with a ban on almost all animal movements except those direct to slaughter.

- Sheep shearing and dipping were identified by Veterinary Risk Assessments as activities that carried significant risks of transmitting FMD. Licensing schemes were introduced in June to minimise the risks. A recent Veterinary Risk Assessment identified sheep scanning as a risk and that is also now a licensed activity.

DEFRA COMMENTS TO INQUIRIES ON FOOT-AND-MOUTH DISEASE (FMD): WELFARE OF ANIMALS

- The Government is committed to high animal welfare standards.

- FMD seriously compromises the welfare of affected animals.

- Elliott Morley established a special Consultative Group of animal welfare bodies for FMD to ensure that animal welfare concerns could be fast-tracked.

- All animals culled during the current FMD outbreak were required to be killed in accordance with the Welfare of Animals (Slaughter or Killing) Regulations 1995 (WASK). Veterinary officers of the State Veterinary Service enforce these regulations outside slaughterhouses. With the growing scale of the culling operation, further detailed instructions were issued on 27 March to all those involved in the cull emphasising their responsibilities under WASK to ensure that all animals were dealt with humanely. To the best of DEFRA's knowledge the vast majority of animals were dealt with humanely and in compliance with WASK. The few cases brought to DEFRA's attention where it was alleged that animals had not been dealt with humanely have been investigated and appropriate action taken.

- On 6 March, MAFF issued advisory leaflets on cattle, sheep and goats and pigs for farmers concerned about animal welfare problems during the outbreak. Local fact sheets were produced on hill sheep and turning out cattle.

- Inability to move animals can lead to a reduction in welfare standards due to lack of fodder, care, shelter or overcrowding. A balance has to be struck between the risk of spreading FMD and welfare benefits of movement. In this regard, the following measures were taken:

- From 8 March, grazing was allowed on land set aside under the Arable Area Payments Scheme where livestock could not be moved due to FMD restrictions. The grazing of eligible crops during the establishment stage was also allowed.

- On 9 March, arrangements were introduced to allow movements of animals under licence on welfare grounds across roads on the same holding and between local holdings under the same ownership subject to certain restrictions and conditions.

- On 19 March, arrangements were introduced for movements of animals under licence over longer distances, also subject to restrictions and conditions.

- On 22 March, the Livestock Welfare Disposal Scheme was opened to maintain high standards of welfare on premises under FMD restrictions. The Scheme provides, where there is an existing problem or one likely to arise within four weeks which is confirmed by a private veterinary surgeon, for the removal and disposal of animals for which the Government will bear the cost and a payment is made for eligible animals. The Scheme was specifically extended to light lambs in September and October.

- From 11 May, licensed movements of cattle, sheep and goats to common grazings were allowed. Licensing arrangements were subsequently put in place to allow the dipping and shearing of sheep.

- From 23 May, movements of animals from premises under Form D restrictions were allowed.

- From 21 June, animals could be moved for veterinary treatment and emergency special needs under Animal Treatment Licenses.

- From 5 July, cattle, sheep and goats could be moved from open hills and moors for shearing or other essential husbandry purposes.

- Subsequent changes were made to facilitate the issue of licences and to extend the types of movement allowed. Finally, a new system of licensing movements by local authorities was introduced from 17 September for FMD free counties; 24 September for animals other than sheep in at risk or higher risk counties and on 1 October for sheep in at risk and higher risk counties. A new sole occupancy licence was introduced on 6 October for movements between holdings under sole occupation within a 10km radius. These movements can be for either welfare or commercial reasons.

DEFRA COMMENTS TO INQUIRIES ON FOOT-AND-MOUTH DISEASE (FMD): COMPENSATION FOR THE COMPULSORY SLAUGHTER OF LIVESTOCK

- All farmers are paid market value as compensation for any animals slaughtered for FMD disease control purposes and over £1 billion has been paid to farmers so far in this outbreak. In addition compensation is paid for any feedingstuffs or any other materials destroyed or seized as being contaminated, which cannot be satisfactorily disinfected.

- The Department appoints a qualified independent valuer to advise on valuation. However, the owner of the animals may, within 14 days of receiving the valuation, give notice that he disputes the valuation. In these circumstances, the matter may be referred to an arbitrator appointed jointly by the owner and DEFRA or by an arbitrator appointed by the President of the Royal Institution of Chartered Surveyors.

- To speed up the valuation process (and hence the speed with which animals were killed), a change was made to the valuation procedure to allow owners of animals to be slaughtered to receive a standard valuation in respect of each animal with an option to elect for market valuation. This facility was made available on 22 March and was withdrawn from 30 July.

- The Animal Health (Amendment) Bill which is now before Parliament will adjust the arrangements for compensation for animals from farms which are infected with the disease. 75% of the value of the animals before they became infected will be payable, with the remaining 25% subject to an assessment of whether the farmer has acted in ways which put his stock at risk or which risk spreading the disease.

DEFRA COMMENTS TO INQUIRIES ON FOOT-AND-MOUTH DISEASE (FMD): CLEANSING AND DISINFECTION (C AND D) OF PREMISES

- All premises where animals have been slaughtered for disease control purposes are required to have completed preliminary disinfection as soon as practicable after the slaughter and disposal of the carcasses. DEFRA bears the cost of this preliminary disinfection.

- Before premises can be restocked with animals, they are required to undergo secondary cleansing and disinfection (C and D) to the satisfaction of DEFRA veterinary staff. DEFRA normally pays the costs of secondary C and D, providing farms are in a reasonable state of cleanliness and repair, there are no health and safety implications for those concerned and the costs incurred are proportionate to the individual farm situation. In the small number of cases where secondary C and D does not take place, the premises are required to remain under restrictions for twelve months.

- On current progress, it is expected that secondary C and D will be completed on nearly all premises by the middle of

February 2002. Nearly 300 of those premises eligible will not undergo secondary C and D, e.g. because of the disproportionate costs involved, farmers leaving agriculture or not restocking, poor state of the farm, health and safety implications.

- The total cost of C and D (including preliminary C and D but excluding ash removal, seized and destroyed items, pyre building, field reinstatement, slurry disposal etc) is estimated to total about £245m, roughly £35k per premise throughout the Country. Currently, costs amount to about £230m (including those completed, and to date on those currently undergoing C and D). This compares with the estimate of £875m in total, £100k per farm, that was being suggested in mid July, and based on comparable Swine Fever costs and relatively limited details of completed C and D on FMD premises.

- The £245m and £230m are still subject to some refinement as final invoices are awaited, disputed invoices resolved and wrongly attributed non-C and D costs are apportioned elsewhere.

- Within these figures, there continues to be regional variations due to size and complexity of farms, the number of premises where C and D was completed early on with a significant proportion of the work undertaken by contractors with higher rates rather than farmers themselves, etc.

- Since 5 August, with renegotiated contracts in place, farmers have been encouraged to undertake the work themselves wherever possible. Many farmers have taken advantage of this opportunity and this has resulted in a reduction (significant in some cases) in average costs, both on those where C and D was suspended at the end of July, and on new premises where work commenced post 5 August.

DEFRA COMMENTS TO INQUIRIES ON FOOT-AND-MOUTH DISEASE (FMD): IMPORT CONTROLS

- There can be no guarantee that no exotic disease will be imported, no matter how stringent our controls. It remains vital that farmers take effective biosecurity measures to minimise the possibility of spread of any disease.

- Imports of meat into any EU state from a third country must conform with EU rules, setting strict conditions and veterinary certification. Plus, meat consignments must be presented on arrival to a Border Inspection Post (BIP) where all consignments are subject to documentary and identity checks and at least 20% of consignments undergo physical checks. The performance of BIPs is audited by the European Commission's Food and Veterinary Office and monitored by DEFRA.

- Where imports are of food, DEFRA is advised by the Food Standards Agency, which is responsible for issues of food safety. In light of current concerns about illegal imports of food of animal origin, the Food Standards Agency has written to port health authorities and local authorities to ensure continued vigilance and checks on imported products both at the point of import and at the retail level.

- It is recognised that illegal imports of meat do arise, mainly by (a) individual travellers bringing small quantities in their luggage and (b) traders hiding meat in containers ostensibly holding other products. Detection of the latter relies on spot checks, usually by HM Customs.

- Have taken the following steps to improve action against illegal imports:

Improved publicity:
- Arranged for posters to be put up at main airports advising incoming passengers what can be brought in legally;
- Provided information to travellers via airlines, travel agents and British Embassies abroad;

Improved enforcement powers:
- Our national regulations have been amended to assist local authorities in seizing suspected illegal imports when they are found at point of sale;

Improved information sharing:
- Established improved procedures for sharing information about illegal activities amongst the departments and enforcement authorities involved (DEFRA, HM Customs & Excise, Port Health Authorities & Local Authorities);

Improved analysis of the problem:
- We are building up a database of details to improve the targeting of enforcement resources to where the risks are greatest;
- These measures are being kept under review and the Government will continue to make improvements as necessary. For example, we are considering the possible use of sniffer dogs and x-ray machines at ports and airports.

DEFRA COMMENTS TO INQUIRIES ON FOOT-AND-MOUTH DISEASE (FMD): THE IMPACT ON AGRICULTURE

- Disease has clearly had an acute adverse impact on the farming industry.

- Government announced on 8 May a range of measures amounting to £15.4m to support farmers; consisting of

- £10.4m for an enhanced Farm Business Advice Service (FBAS) offering up to 5 days of free business advice for farmers whose livestock have been slaughtered under the foot and mouth control measures;

- £2m in grant aid made available under a new round of the Agricultural Development Scheme, to improve marketing performance and competitiveness of sectors affected by foot and mouth;

- £3m for a targeted trade development and market campaign, made available through Food from Britain who will co-ordinate their campaign with the Countryside Agency, Meat and Livestock Commission and others with an active interest.

- **The Rural Development Service ran 23 seminars during July and August for farmers who had their stock culled (in addition to the FBAS visit) to provide advice on business and farm operational issues. 2016 delegates attended. A regional contact service has been established to provide further advice and advice.**

- **All this is in addition to the over £1 billion paid out to farmers in compensation for animals slaughtered due to foot and mouth disease.**

- DEFRA has made available approaching £1m over 2000/01 and 2001/02 to support farmers through a Rural Stress Action Plan (RSAP), part of the Prime Minister's Action Plan for Farming.

- Further funding of £400,000 for the second RSAP was announced on 3 August to continue the work being carried out. The RSAP Group represents an unprecedented partnership between Government, the voluntary mental health sector (including the Samaritans) and national farming organisations and aims to deliver support to and make a real difference to those in distress.

- The Government has funded the Rural Stress Information Network (RSIN) to establish a network of support available to people in rural communities who are suffering from stress. The network includes professional health care staff and voluntary organisations with relevant expertise (Samaritans, MIND etc) together with legal, financial and business support.

DEFRA COMMENTS TO INQUIRIES ON FOOT-AND-MOUTH DISEASE (FMD): MOVEMENT OF ANIMALS

- On 23 February, as soon as it became apparent that the disease was not confined to the area around the first outbreaks in Essex, the whole of Great Britain was declared to be a controlled area. On veterinary advice an immediate standstill was imposed on the movement of all FMD susceptible animals in Great Britain.

- Animal movements were subsequently allowed subject to licence and in accordance with the terms and conditions of such licences. These have been allowed in accordance with veterinary risk assessments, location and the changing disease situation.

- Movement direct to slaughter for human consumption at approved slaughterhouses under licence from a local authority was allowed from 2 March for animals outside Infected Areas. Subsequently, the scope of these movements was extended as follows:

- From 23 April, animals were allowed to move to slaughter from within an Infected Area to a slaughterhouse in the same Infected Area (unless the holding of origin was within a Protection Zone).

- From 3 May animals from farms in Protection Zones (once 15 days had passed since the preliminary disinfection of the relevant Infected Place) were allowed to move to slaughter in the same Infected Area.

- From 21 June, animals from farms in an Infected Area were able to move to slaughter outside the Infected Area as long as they were not from holdings in a 10 km Surveillance Zone around an Infected Place within the first 30 days after disease had been confirmed and subject to various additional conditions including a distance limit of 250 km on the journey to the slaughterhouse and a requirement that the slaughterhouse could not be in a Provisionally Free Area.

- From 28 June, animals were allowed to move to a licensed collecting centre before further movement to an approved slaughterhouse.

- Additionally movements of animals under licence other than to slaughter for human consumption have been allowed as follows:

- On 9 March, arrangements were introduced to allow movements of animals under licence on welfare grounds across roads on the same holding and between local holdings under the same ownership subject to certain restrictions and conditions. Initially these were for welfare reasons only but from the end of April, such movements could be for general husbandry and management purposes.

- On 19 March, arrangements were introduced for movements of animals under licence over longer distances, also subject to restrictions and conditions.

- From 11 May, licensed movements of sheep to common grazings were allowed. Bulls, boars and rams for breeding could also be moved under the Longer Distance Scheme without a qualifying welfare need.

- From 23 May, movements of animals from premises under Form D restrictions were allowed.

- From 21 June, animals could be moved for veterinary treatment and emergency special needs under Animal Treatment Licenses.

- From 5 July, sheep could be moved from open hills and moors for shearing or other essential husbandry purposes.

- From 1 August, the Over Thirty Months Scheme has been re-opened for cattle.

- A new system of licensing movements by local authorities was introduced from 17 September for FMD free counties; 24 September for animals other than sheep in at risk or higher risk counties and on 1 October for sheep in at risk and higher risk counties. A new sole occupancy licence was introduced on 6 October for movements between holdings under sole occupation within a 10km radius. These movements can be for either welfare or commercial reasons.

DEFRA COMMENTS TO INQUIRIES ON FOOT-AND-MOUTH DISEASE (FMD): THE IMPACT ON THE RURAL ECONOMY

Short Term Survival

- The most effective way to help is to bring the disease to an end as quickly as possible and to re-open the countryside to visitors. But we also need to help affected rural businesses cope. We are doing this through:

- Deferring tax, VAT and National Insurance payments, without interest charges, for severely affected businesses (22,000 businesses having over £191m deferred as at 27 November);

- Deferring and/or giving hardship relief (writing off) rate payments through new funding arrangements to meet centrally 95-98% of costs for rural local authorities to help businesses under £12,000 Rateable Value (worth up to £3,000 over 9 months), and businesses under £50,000 RV (worth up to £12,000) in the worst affected areas;

- Helping businesses adjust to FMD impacts by making grants, from the Business Recovery Fund (£74m), run by the RDAs, which is funding business improvements, training and loan interest costs (5,600 grant approvals worth £22m have been issued with £9m actually paid to individual businesses); BRF also supports local/regional tourism promotion and rural regeneration projects which help bring visitors back to rural areas more quickly;

- Fast-tracking and prioritising other measures to speed up rural regeneration, for example rapid introduction of mandatory rate relief for pubs, garages, and other food shops in small settlements, and extending the Market Towns programme to include towns badly affected by FMD;

- Helping small businesses without security access bank lending by extending the Small Firms Loan Guarantee Scheme to new sectors and creating new flexibilities on interest and capital repayments. (Take-up has been very low, however.)

- Have matched nearly £14m in donations from the public to charitable organisations that are helping farmers and rural communities hit by FMD. A further £2m extension to the scheme was announced on 6 November.

Longer term rural revival

- The Haskins and Rural Task Force reports, published 18 October, contain wide range of recommendations for sustainable rural recovery. The Government has responded to these.

- Rural White Paper: fast-tracking of further elements.

- ERDP - seven-year programme will help projects which will contribute to the creation of diverse and competitive agricultural and forestry sectors.

- Action plans being developed in worst affected areas: Cumbria Rural Action Zone and Devon Recovery Plan.

DEFRA COMMENTS TO INQUIRIES ON FOOT-AND-MOUTH DISEASE (FMD): ACCESS TO THE COUNTRYSIDE

- The top priority is to beat the disease and, to this end, tight biosecurity is essential.

- A precautionary response was understandable in the early days of the FMD outbreak and most local authorities made use of powers then available to impose blanket closures on the rights of way network.

- Regulatory controls over public access to the countryside must be proportionate to the risk of spreading FMD, taking account of the prevailing disease situation, and a risk based approach was adopted. Veterinary Risk Assessments have been reviewed and revised as the outbreak progressed.

- On 18 May, the veterinary risk assessment was revised and recommended that regulatory controls on public use of rights of way should be confined to agricultural premises and agricultural land within 3 km Protection Zones round an Infected Place. Elsewhere, the public were encouraged to accept responsibility to owners and occupiers of the land they crossed by having regard to Codes which applied in Infected Areas and elsewhere, e.g. by staying off farmland if they had recently handled farm animals and by avoiding contact with livestock.

- In the light of the revised Veterinary Risk Assessment, on 23 May the Government issued guidance to local authorities in England encouraging the re-opening of footpaths where it was safe to do so, outside 3 km Protection Zones.

- Progress by local authorities towards re-opening their footpaths was slower than anticipated, so on 20 July, following consultation with the local authorities, the Government revoked most remaining blanket right of way closures previously imposed by local authorities.

- Exemptions from the revocation of blanket closures were given to six local authorities worst affected by FMD, for all or part of their areas: Cumbria (whole county), Devon, Durham, Gloucestershire, Herefordshire and Lancashire. These were granted on logistical grounds, as many thousands of footpaths would have had to be re-signed individually as closed.

- The exemptions have been reviewed, and three of the authorities (Devon, Gloucestershire and Herefordshire) have lifted their exemptions by completely re-opening all their footpaths except those across premises remaining under veterinary restrictions. The exemptions for Cumbria, Durham and Lancashire are being considered further in the light of revised veterinary risk assessment and local authority guidance on re-opening footpaths issued on 7 December.

- Given the exceptional circumstances leading to the imposition of Restricted Infected Areas ("Blue Boxes"), Government accepted that footpaths within the boxes should remain closed if such an Area is declared.

- On 7 December, the revised veterinary risk assessment on re-opening public footpaths was issued along with revised Government guidance to local authorities that footpaths, apart from those going through farmyards or buildings, across premises under veterinary restrictions (Form A, 'modified' Form D or FM37B 'article 38' Notices) could be re-opened subject to specific criteria.

- Local authorities were encouraged to work closely with their local DEFRA Divisional Veterinary Managers to establish exactly which footpaths could be re-opened as a result of this development, but no significant further re-openings were expected until that process was completed

- A media campaign was conducted to inform the public about access to the countryside. Key in this was the need to ensure that those wishing to visit the countryside had access to accurate information on the foot and mouth situation. Despite careful media choices to ensure that coverage across England and Wales was as thorough and even as possible, difficulties persisted in the level of accuracy of information available to the public on what was open.

- www.countryside.gov.uk or individual local authority websites also gave more information about footpath re-opening.

- Some concern has been expressed at the mixed message: on the one hand, maintain tight biosecurity; on the other, get visitors back to the countryside. There is no inconsistency between the two. The risks are of a very different order. The current Veterinary Risk Assessment notes that transmission by people has been recorded on many occasions, but those responsible have generally had close contact with animals on infected, and then on uninfected, premises. It is theoretically possible that walkers could carry infection to previously uninfected animals, although there is no evidence that this has actually happened and the risk, if any, is small in comparison to other transmission risks. It also notes that even small risks can be further diminished by appropriate action. Footpath users should continue to observe sensible precautions, including making use of biosecurity measures provided by farmers.

Voices from Devon

Extracts from evidence submitted to the Devon Foot and Mouth Inquiry 2001

Some 380 people and organisations, from Devon and beyond, submitted evidence to the Devon Foot and Mouth Inquiry during its investigations in the late summer and autumn of 2001. Fifty witnesses gave further evidence at the Inquiry's hearings in public held in Exeter over 8th -12th October 2001.

Together, these submissions reflect vividly the experience of individuals, communities and organisations throughout Devon during the worst Foot and Mouth epidemic ever recorded. They also provide a wealth of ideas about how the crisis might have been better tackled and how the social and economic life of the county can recover in the coming years.

The submissions reveal powerful first-hand accounts of what it was like for people to live through the Foot and Mouth crisis and they also contain the sober reflections of many agencies involved in responding to its immense challenge.

In support of the Inquiry's final report, the following pages bring together edited extracts from these accounts. These have in many cases been selected (and considerably shortened in length) from more detailed submissions made to the Devon Inquiry. They should not be read therefore as being representative of the full extent of evidence submitted by a particular person or organisation.

These selections are presented in two sections. Key quotes from people attending the Inquiry Hearings are followed by extracts from written submissions. Details of people and organisations who submitted evidence to the Devon Foot and Mouth Inquiry can be found in an Appendix.

In due course Devon County Council will place a full copy of all evidence submitted to the Inquiry on public deposit in the Devon Record Office to bear permanent witness to the Foot and Mouth crisis of 2001. For now, these extracts are offered to the reader as a compelling tapestry of insights and experiences, a glimpse of what three short words - "Foot and Mouth" - meant for one county.

These then are the *"Voices from Devon"*.

VOICES FROM THE DEVON INQUIRY HEARINGS 8th -12th OCTOBER 2001

It was a disaster from start to finish...MAFF were playing catch up from day one... It was very difficult to obtain information especially in the early days and this only served to feed the rumour mill among farmers... Contiguous culling led to the unnecessary killing of animals, caused great personal distress among farmers and led to MAFF rapidly losing control...

David Hill, Devon County Chairman, National Farmers' Union

• • • • •

Some cattle spent days roaming around the village when they bolted after an attempted MAFF cull... Some took four or five shots to kill... It was chaos and shambles...

William Norman, Knowstone Parish Council

• • • • •

My children had never seen me cry before. They have now... In the space of 24 hours we were advised to move by the MoD and offered holiday accommodation by MAFF... it is clear we were seen as an easy and cheap target... All we want is an apology ... we want it to go away and be restored to how it was.

Mark Tomlinson, Local Resident

• • • • •

We felt as if we were under siege. I am not a farmer but I felt very much the siege mentality... Farmers felt that if there was somebody closer to them who could translate, interpret, advise and reassure, someone they could turn to, that would have been a great help...

Ken Lancaster, Kennerleigh Parish Meeting

• • • • •

I found the lack of direction and advice most disappointing. People were looking to the school for information and we couldn't provide them with any as we were not getting any support ourselves... We felt totally isolated...

Mark Raven, Headteacher, Black Torrington Primary School

• • • • •

Someone needed to take a grip... We needed someone to take government guidance and deploy local resources quickly... Getting accurate information and providing well-grounded feedback is critical to this whole process... It was clear that Government Ministers, however well intentioned, had a lack of understanding of the impact on the ground...

John Varley, Estates Director, Clinton Devon Estates

• • • • •

I couldn't believe how poor communication was... Information was haphazard, often vague or contradictory, or simply just refused... What was really required was a single point of regular, good quality information...

Graham Gilbert, Managing Director, Great Western Radio

• • • • •

There was and is considerable ignorance over how the disease is spread and major pressure to close down the countryside... With hindsight it became clearer that visitors were not a significant factor and therefore some parts of the countryside and vital paths such as the South West Coast path were closed unnecessarily...

Alex Raeder, Senior Land Agent, Devon Region, National Trust

• • • • •

The sooner command and control is established the sooner order can be brought to chaos...This is not a natural responsibility for civil servants and the Foot and Mouth Emergency plans did not look like they had been developed since the last major outbreak... The military should have been brought in sooner, but with a clear remit - a better idea of what they were there to do... Whoever takes the lead in future needs to be better at developing contingency plans and the proper level of training and resources to implement them.

Sir John Evans, Chief Constable, Devon and Cornwall Police

· · · · ·

The images of barbaric killing and primeval disposal of cattle and sheep carcasses have been transmitted around the world... People thought they had gone back to the Dark Ages... I honestly believe we could get the business back next year with effective marketing... But it will not drift back on its own...The challenge for some businesses is to survive until next Easter.

Malcolm Bell, Chief Executive, South West Tourism

· · · · ·

The public got the idea that Devon and Cornwall was closed... As far as the media and the public were concerned, it was essential to get the story over quickly and it was not done.

John Fowler, Chairman, John Fowler Holidays

· · · · ·

Burning pyres were a legitimate news event and became the single most vivid image of Foot and Mouth. It would be naïve to think these images would not get shown... I am very surprised that there wasn't a game plan in place. In any future emergency, effective communications including the new realities of the mass media must be taken into account.

Chris Foreman, Senior Output Editor, Carlton TV

· · · · ·

Closing off access to people to enjoy the Devon environment is what has affected the Devon economy... As the months went by and guidance evolved, that would not be the decision we would take now...

Nick Atkinson, Chief Executive, Dartmoor National Park Authority

· · · · ·

Farming was the bedrock of employment in rural areas and young people are now faced with a struggle to find jobs and homes and have to look seriously at moving out of the area...

Mark Goodman, County Organiser, Devon Federation of Young Farmers

· · · · ·

The pain and fear in our community was palpable. You could feel it coming over the phone... I would get distressed calls at night from people whose husbands had gone out and they didn't know where they were... There is a lot of isolation and psychiatric ill health that exists in the countryside and that is compounded by loneliness and financial worries... It is almost like having mud shovelled on your head and sooner or later you are going to go down.

Rev Paul Fitzpatrick, Northmoor Team Ministry

· · · · ·

Farmers are not a group traditionally likely to access mental health services... But the 'bereavement' associated with the loss of animals and the hopelessness of the situation is likely to lead to desperation and an increased risk of depressive illness.

Dr Mike Owen, Director of Public Health, North and East Devon Health Authority

· · · · ·

Unless fodder can be brought in from outside we are heading for a disastrous welfare problem this winter – for animals and humans...

Peter Clarke, Farm Crisis Network

VOICES FROM THE WRITTEN SUBMISSIONS TO THE DEVON INQUIRY

(submitted August - October 2001)

I found the Foot and Mouth an invisible enemy worse than the war in 1939. I was fortunate as most of the vets who came to visit my small flock of sheep were clean, coming from Exeter in the mornings, but fears were very much to the fore when they came later in the day from Highampton or Hatherleigh.   I often woke up in the night crying.   At one time I could see eight fires burning.   Luckily the Foot and Mouth passed me by and my animals were saved.

Mrs Watson, Beaworthy

• • • • •

The village was surrounded by outbreaks of the Foot and Mouth Disease and is also situated on the edge of the Ash Moor Burial Site with the access being at the lower end of the village.

At no time was the Parish Council consulted or informed by MAFF or any other agency (with the exception of one letter from Devon County Council) regarding any matters appertaining to this crisis.

The Parish Council, therefore, was unable to address the concerns and anxieties of worried parishioners.   The workload on officials of the Parish Council has been tremendous as they unsuccessfully sought answers to parishioners' concerns.   Due to many changes of personnel at MAFF/DEFRA there has been no continuity.

Meeth Parish Council

• • • • •

Financially: Income stopped as unable to sell stock.   When able to sell, animals not at best - so lower sale value, lower price and extra costs.   No provision by Government to replace income or support farmers at all.

Emotionally: Myself, my husband and 2 children frequently in tears, constantly tired, frequently unable to see any form of light at end of tunnel. Support given by friends, family and local people kept us going.

Socially: All social activities stopped: pub skittles, bingos, YFC meetings etc.   Did not see anyone outside farm. Family worried about visiting.

Ms Boundy, Tiverton

• • • • •

I am not a farmer or a landowner but the Foot and Mouth outbreak here in Devon affected my family and me more than most.

How many farmers had less than 24 hours to vacate their homes; possibly never to return? How many landowners gave their children an hour to pack one small cardboard box of toys before being forced to leave their homes like World War II refugees?

The hell that my wife, children and I had to endure can only be imagined.   The misery was down solely to the arrogance, rudeness, thoughtlessness and sheer bullying of one organisation - MAFF.

On the evening of 5th April a representative of the MOD phoned me and asked if I would be available the following morning to speak to regarding some roadworks on the lane that runs outside our house.   This, needless to say, seemed strange so I contacted some of my neighbours who joined my wife and me at our house the following day.

As we sat in our sitting room we were told that: MAFF and the MOD were to tarmac 'our private' lane for a distance of approximately 600 metres, from right through a field gate to an area of 100 acres which was culm grass, tarmac the huge portion of that 100 acres, dig 18 burial pits each the size of a football pitch, slaughter animals on site and then bury up to 400,000 animals there. These animals would be transported to the Ash Moor burial site in upwards of 10,000 lorries, each passing within 6 ft of our front door. The MOD Officer strongly advised us to leave as soon as possible as life would not be "worth living" and that work would start the next morning - less than 24 hours hence.

In a direct line these pits were to be and three are within 200 metres of our house. All this information given to us in such an unexpected manner was met by stunned silence. I am an ex-Metropolitan Police Officer; it takes a lot to upset me. In the room with me was an ex-Army Officer who has spent many years in Northern Ireland, two farmers, a nurse and a couple more of our neighbours - not a group of people to be easily shocked but we were.

The Army Officer (who through the next few weeks of upset and mayhem we were forced to endure was the only honourable person we dealt with) did not know the lane that it was intended to tarmac was private. He organised at our request a Public Meeting the following morning - the 7th - at Petrockstowe Village Hall.

At the meeting attended by many hundreds of people and media I tried to speak on three occasions but burst into tears of sadness, frustration, helplessness and anger each time.

After the meeting I had an appointment at our house with a surveyor.   He told me point blank that our 130-year-old lodge house would not stand the vibration of 10,000 lorries and that was always hoping that one did not hit the house. The house would not be habitable again - ever.   Once this ill-conceived, panic driven, dangerous experiment was revealed to the general public in all its horror a tide of opposition began.

Meetings started with MAFF and Imerys, the French company that own the local clay works upon which the land covered by Ash Moor stands to try to find an alternative access route that did not necessitate coming past our house. The company sold MAFF the land and if they had also given them access to the clay works in the first place instead of making them try to come down the private lane I would not have had to cuddle my three children nightly as they cried themselves to sleep.   Negotiations lasted for over a week during which time my wife and I had to find a house to move to - MAFF didn't - prepare our children to not only move but possibly never to return and to take turns sleeping as the lack of trust we had in MAFF led us strongly to believe they would just steamroller a road past our house in the middle of the night.

At 8 a.m. one morning the week following our first notification of this whole project, my two sons ran into our bedroom crying that there were lorries and workmen outside our house. There were in fact steamrollers, a JCB, a tarmac machine, lorries, vans and lots of people.   Before I could stop them, the JCB took the top six inches off the lane. I was told point blank they were there to turn our un-metalled lane into a tarmac road.   Our solicitor was quickly on scene and work ceased though calming a distraught 13, 10 and 6 year old took a lot longer.

To now cut a very long, frightening, upsetting story short. MAFF finally gained access to the clay works but at what cost? Financially, who knows? Emotionally, we know. My children had never seen me cry before April 2001. They have now. Lots.

If it were not for the fact that my wife and I love each other so very much and support one another to be good parents, I dread to think how this could have affected my family.   Short term: my children didn't eat, sleep, learn, play or do anything 'normally'. I sympathise with every refugee I see on the News now; like them I was living in fear for my family and home.

Long term: I don't know what effect it will have on any of us but like the 'Sword of Damocles' the Ash Moor pit is still hanging over us ready to be used on the whim of politicians.

No one knows what we have been through. To lose your animals must be soul destroying but to have your home ripped out from under you at a moment's notice is mind, body and soul destroying. Many, many farmers, some unknown to me, phoned to give me support and for that we will be eternally grateful.   If it were not for our friends - who knows what might have been - or will be.

Mr Tomlinson, Petrockstowe

The Borough is the largest geographical District Council area in Devon and one of the largest Districts in England. It covers an area of almost 116,000 hectares, which is slightly larger than the area contained within the M25 London orbital motorway. However, its population is less than 50,000 people and it is therefore the most sparsely populated area of Southern England.

The first outbreak of the Foot and Mouth Disease in the South West of England was confirmed at Highampton in West Devon on the 24th February 2001. From then until June 17th, when the last outbreak occurred at Bondleigh, West Devon, there have been 72 cases in the Borough involving 34,000 animals and larger number of farms subject to contiguous culls. There have been 96 animal disposal sites in West Devon, nearly all pyre sites.

Mr Incoll, West Devon Borough Council

• • • • •

Being within the 3 kilometre zones of several Foot and Mouth Disease infections, my holding (40 sheep) was inspected nine times by MAFF vets between the 28th March and 22nd May. Neighbouring farms, all within the same zones, with stocks ranging from 250 to 4,500 animals (pigs, cattle and sheep) were not inspected or were only visited much later in that period when they applied for movement licences.

In Easter week there were 10,000 animals heaped in the gateways of fields in Chulmleigh/Meshaw parishes, all blatantly exposed to public view. The trauma of such unnecessary exposure is reflected in the need for the local school to write to the GCSE Examination Boards warning that the concentration and performance of local children has been significantly affected by the management of Foot and Mouth Disease.

Locally, detailed observation of the delayed incineration of infected carcasses and varying wind directions more accurately predicted the occurrences of fresh outbreaks. Local pyres were seen to smoulder, at times barely warming some carcasses on the periphery of the fire. Dark smoke from coal and impregnated timber rose rapidly from the fires but separated from a steamy, fatty white vapour that drifted close to the ground. Local motorists driving through the smoke and vapour found small patches of unburned flesh on bonnets and the tyres of their vehicles.

Dr Pay, Chulmleigh

• • • • •

The initial impact for many young people was disruption to education. This has impacted on those at school, FE Colleges and other specialist colleges. Young people were unable to attend lessons and had to cancel appointments with personal advisers.

There are four areas where Foot and Mouth has impacted upon young people. These are:

1. The emotional impact of being on a farm where all your animals have been slaughtered on your doorstep, literally in some cases. Living on a farm 24 hours a day with parents who are stressed fearing for their future could not have been easy. There has been a considerable impact on those young people who have lived near a funeral pyre. In the Holsworthy area you could see up to 12 funeral pyres going at any one time. The smell was very unpleasant and a constant reminder of what was going on.

2. Isolation was the next issue. Rural young people find this to be a big issue for them in normal times but Foot and Mouth made this many times worse. Farmers were so terrified of getting the disease that they barricaded themselves and their families in for several weeks. Even when the initial fears subsided, young people were allowed back to school but were not allowed out in the evenings. Some were actually sent away to stay with relatives until Foot and Mouth subsided.

3. For those who were sitting exams this was a particularly difficult time. There is little doubt that many will have been affected and this will have a knock-on effect on their future.

4. Career choices for some changed in the space of a few weeks. Whilst farming and related industries have been undergoing a fundamental change over the last few years, Foot and Mouth will have acted as a catalyst. Many will now not have the option of going home to work on the farm and they will need support to plan their futures. Some will feel trapped in a position where they have to look outside farming but loyalty to the family means they stay on, often working for little, if any, pay.

Ms Rudge, Connexions Cornwall and Devon Ltd

The impact on the Trust's farming tenants generally has reflected the impact of the disease on the wider farming community within Devon.

We are particularly pleased with the way in which the NFU in Devon conducted itself. It provided good advice, worked with partners and the excellent communication of their bulletins on a regular basis was a help to us all. I regret to say this was in contrast with that received from MAFF (now DEFRA).

In addition to the impact on farming, the Trust was severely affected by closure of its houses and gardens, and countryside car parks. Whilst some houses were able to open in time for Easter, many of our major properties missed out on what is one of the peak periods for visitors. By the end of April visitors were down by 64% on the previous year, and at the end of May 42%.

The Trust is still assessing the total cost of the outbreak on all its properties but our most up to date estimates indicate our loss to be approximately £800,000. If one uses the multiplier in our 'Valuing our Environment' document, the real loss to the economy in Devon is £5.2 million.

Mr Cook, Devon Region, National Trust

• • • • •

Effect of Foot and Mouth on Farm Accommodation Businesses

General pattern: End February to Easter, enquiries stopped, cancellations flooded in. Cash flow dried up, so operators unable to advertise in 2002 brochures, and enhancement of facilities put on hold.

Summer: Farms near coasts, cities or with own web sites had a good July and August. Others had a patchy July, but generally a good August.

Autumn: Very patchy. Some farms getting better bookings than last year. Others are well down. Things are well below normal for many farms and the feeling is that walkers and cyclists are not coming in their normal numbers.

Percentages by which Bed and Breakfast bookings were down in 2001 against same month in 2000 for Dartmoor:

March   -   91% down
April   -   81% down
Easter   -   77% down
May   -   65% down

Mr Head, Devon Farms Accommodation

• • • • •

The Estate has been affected in many different ways; emotional, operational and financial. We firmly believe that there are some 'positives' to be taken out of the nightmare of the past few months. From the Estates' point of view, we are working as a team like never before to find new structures and better ways of working. We are committed to crafting a new model for our farm and related businesses, which is relevant to Devon with its unique set of circumstances and opportunities.

The most significant impact on the Estate was in North Devon on the Heanton Estate where all bar one of the Home and tenant farms suffered livestock culls. Lord Clinton's herd of pedigree Red Devon cattle with lineage dating back to 1888 was slaughtered as part of these culls.

As far as one of our farms was concerned it is difficult to think how the process could have been improved. The diagnosis was confirmed late afternoon on Thursday and the animals despatched immediately. The next stage, Friday, the diagnosis was confirmed by a second vet, there being some query as to whether it was Foot and Mouth Disease. The slaughter team had arrived by mid-morning; it consisted of a large team of drovers, slaughter men and an army liaison person. The work was done quickly, efficiently, with respect, and to a high standard of professionalism. In mid-afternoon, when the work had been completed, a MAFF technician, contractor representative and Environment Agency representative arrived to deal with disposal arrangements. They quickly established that burial was not an option. A pyre site, together with access was agreed upon, having particular regard to technical and other sensitive considerations.

Mr Varley, Clinton Devon Estates

Survey of Village Shops in Devon - August 2001

Shop A   Turnover approximately 10% down between February and August and up to 30% down for a ten-day period over crisis point.

Shop B   Turnover between March and July was 20% down and could have been worse had the shop not adapted and organised a delivery service to affected farms.

Shop C   Shop turnover is up to 30% down and diverse activities established to exploit tourism have all ceased.

Shop D   Turnover down 10% February to July.

Shop E   Turnover down 20% for February and March but now approaching pre-Foot and Mouth levels.

Shop F   Turnover is down approximately 15% and probably more in real terms.

Shop G   Foot and Mouth crisis halted progress resulting in 20%-25% downturn.

Shop H   Shop turnover down 20%-25% during peak three weeks of crisis. Now recovered to approximately 5%-10% deficit.

Shop I   Shop turnover down 50% and one staff member laid off.

Shop J   Reductions of up to 40% in shop turnover.

Mr Geeves, St Austell, Cornwall

• • • • •

From time to time I am paid by a natural history and environmental survey company to carry out field surveys of invertebrate animal species.   The surveys are particularly important in Spring and early Summer for such insects as solitary bees (some nationally rare) which are key habitat indicators.

The Foot and Mouth brought such investigations to a standstill. Not only did I lose useful income, but more importantly, the firm that uses me was hit financially as it lost several important contracts without warning and is now in difficulties. (It employs 5 fulltime and 4 part-time like me).

Mr Haes, Hayle, Cornwall

• • • • •

From the 22nd April to the 4th May we had to suffer the relentless and constant smoke and fumes from the pyre approximately a 1/4 mile away. This affected our health in the short term and who knows about the long term.

The pyre was lit on Sunday, the 22nd April, about 200 yards from the nearest homes. The first that we knew about it was the police informing us to close our doors and windows (this was after the fire had been lit). The whole area was covered with thick black smoke for days and also noxious fumes.

On the 26th April we telephoned our District Councillor. He told us his hands were tied, he was not even allowed near the site of the pyre and that, as we also agreed, MAFF were a law unto themselves and did not have to account for their actions. In the meantime a friend who lives next to the farm in question informed us that lorries were going to the farm with carcasses from other farms in the area.   Again the local populace were not informed. All we could do was put up with the fumes day and night. We were kept totally in the dark. We suffered respiratory problems and a feeling of weakness for several days. So did several other people we spoke to. We were also told that the air quality was not being monitored. We also had a large vegetable garden and we could not eat our produce because of the fallout from the fire.

Mr Trainor and Ms Norman, Barnstaple

• • • • •

I am a semi-retired farmer with approximately 55 acres of land. At the time of the outbreak of Foot and Mouth in the village I had some of my fields in use for grass growing and two fields, on the eastern edge of my property, in use as grazing for 56 sheep and their lambs. Lambing was almost finished. These sheep belonged to a man who had rented my grass for grazing during the winter and had been unable to move or tend them due to the Foot and Mouth restrictions. I and my wife had dealt with the lambing ourselves.

We also had 36 cattle in a large stock shed in the centre of the property. Eight of these were mine, the rest belonged to my daughter who has a farm near Exeter. We were bringing them on for her, they were in calf Friesians and were to be her future dairy cows.

On Sunday, 13th May, I was driving my tractor in one of the eastern fields next to a field behind the Masons' Arms Inn which I call the 'Glebe Ground'. At around 8 p.m. I heard the sound of gunshots coming from that field. They sounded like a shotgun. When I drove close to the hedge I saw five cattle dead, three men who I didn't know wearing white overalls, and the rest of the cattle in the field were charging around the field. I shouted to the men and the cattle then ran towards me and found their way through a thick Devon bank and thorn hedge, which included three strands of barbed wire, six in places. They say that animals do not have facial expressions. I shall take the look of terror on the faces of those poor beasts to my grave.

I have been a farmer or engaged in farming for all of my life but I have never experienced such a sight. Nineteen eventually got into my field amongst the sheep. Their eyes were staring, they were panting with their tongues hanging out and many were bleeding from wounds caused by the barbed wire or shot. I couldn't get close enough to them.

Attempts the next day to move the cattle from my field all failed due to their agitated state. At one stage, with no one closer than 50 metres and no white suits in sight, the animals forced their way through another lesser hedge.

Despite suggestions on less stressful ways to dispose of these 19 cattle, they were all killed by a marksman on the 14th May. (I have heard that two other cattle from the same field escaped into other farms nearby).

Mr Willmetts, Knowstone

· · · · ·

I have two pedigree pet Berkshire pigs (rare breeds), litter brothers, Gordon and Gregory. I am a widow and I have no family or living relatives. Gordon and Gregory are my children. During the Foot and Mouth crisis I suffered so much stress, worry, sleepless nights etc., my health was badly affected and I required treatment from my doctor.

I bought the pigs last year on the advice of friends and my doctor to help me get over the loss of my husband, two friends from cancer, two much loved horses and my husband's much loved Berkshire boar, Toby (all these losses happened in a short space of time). I could not face losing Gordon and Gregory.

Mrs Trumper, Farringdon

· · · · ·

We were not affected personally or financially in any way by the Foot and Mouth Disease crisis but my husband is a retired bank manager, and up until his retirement many of his customers were farmers (most now retired). In our experience 99% of the farmers are of the honest "salt of the earth" types with great integrity.

Mrs Chave, West Hill

· · · · ·

We are service engineers, self employed, repairing domestic appliances. At the outbreak of Foot and Mouth the telephone more or less stopped ringing for five months. August was fairly busy and September is slow. We lived down a farm lane and we are sure that this is a contributing factor as is the slowdown in rural economy.

Mrs Tappin, Pyworthy

· · · · ·

Up until 1994 there was regular contact between Devon County Council's Emergency Planning Service and MAFF for war planning purposes. Since then contact has continued, but has been infrequent. I am not aware that my predecessor was ever contacted to discuss a MAFF Foot and Mouth Contingency Plan, and such a Plan has never been brought to my notice.

Mr Thomasson, Devon County Council

Divisions occurred within people and between different groups - "us and them". The "us" became narrower and smaller - only the immediate family. Thus psychological isolation exacerbated physical isolation. People withdrew from the nurturing of the community. The dangerous "not us" became wider and bigger: farmers, walkers; MAFF/DEFRA; those with no bio-security and those with excellent bio-security; those who left, those who remained; organic farmers, postmen, people with dogs; horse drivers and horse riders; children at school and not; open pubs and closed pubs; those compensated and those not; those who cheated and those who played straight. Suspicion, guilt, panic, fear and abandonment were all apparent. What is left is lack of confidence, depression, lack of ability to respond, and despair.

Miss Roberts, Holne

. . . . .

218 dairy cows and calves killed in contiguous cull. Left in farmyards for 16 days. No payment for seven weeks. C and D work ongoing still. Payments few and far between. Trying to keep workman on.

Animals must be killed in 24 hours – ours were 5 days.

Animals must be destroyed in 24 hours – ours were 17 days.

A and L Gifford, Milton Damarel

. . . . .

Hunting ceased immediately the Foot and Mouth epidemic started to develop and this led to an immediate loss of revenue of approximately 10% of the Hunt's annual takings. The epidemic also led to the cancellation of a number of hunt events, most noticeably the popular dog show in April which was rescheduled and then subsequently abandoned. The event should have provided a platform for a number of local traders. Our social events, such as the hunt puppy show in July have also been cancelled. The hound breeding programme was also stopped, resulting in only two of our own hounds being bred to join the pack next season instead of the usual eight to ten hounds.

We now face the prospect of no hunting taking place from the start of our season until at least Christmas time, possibly later. This puts our organisation in financial peril.

Mr Jewitt, Stoke Hill Beagles

. . . . .

We operate 14 self-catering Holiday Parks in Devon and Cornwall and accommodate in the region of 300,000 visitors each year. My company entailed approximately £1.5m in unnecessary vacancies for accommodation compared to the previous three-year occupancy. The point I wish to make emphatically is despite Foot and Mouth there was no need for these visitors to have stayed away. When we were able to talk to clients who had booked it was easy to explain to them that Devon was not closed and seaside holiday parks continue to operate normally with virtually no inconvenience to our guests. The impression the public received through the media and so on was that Devon and Cornwall were closed and that they could not come on holiday.

We are 100% behind the farming community and their fight against Foot and Mouth. We realise their problems and recognise that without the farmers the Devon countryside would not be as attractive as it is now. I would like to say we acknowledge the splendid work of Malcolm Bell of South West Tourism who with a minimum of support tried to bring common sense to bear.

Mr Fowler, Ilfracombe

. . . . .

As the Headteacher of a small rural primary school I am concerned about the psychological health of the children living in this area who have been exposed to the effects of the Foot and Mouth outbreak. My concerns are:

- The long-term effects on children who witnessed the wholesale slaughter of their parents/grandparents/near relatives' flocks and herds.

- The effects that social and emotional isolation has had on children being surrounded by adults who were themselves so devastated by events that they were unable to help their own children through the crisis.

- The effects on children who in the midst of the trauma were sent away to stay with relatives or friends.

- The effects of the sight and smells of slaughtered animals, given that many of the animals were 'personal friends' of the children through perhaps having watched their birth, bottle-fed lambs/calves or kept them in the farm kitchen for the first few days of life.

Mrs Rudman, High Bickington Primary School

• • • • •

Being wholesalers in the sock and thermal underwear market we have been hit very hard by the closure of the footpaths and open areas. Even now, with areas being opened up again, sales are still badly affected due to the public not having walked all summer and therefore not needing to replace their equipment. Sales dropped from £84,187 in the period March - July 2000 to £37,383 during the same period in 2001.

Mr Moore, Ottery St Mary

• • • • •

We are only small farmers. We have lived within the 3 kilometre zone of Foot and Mouth Disease since the beginning of the outbreak. We have lived through virtually every negative emotion known to man during that time - fear, anger, frustration, despair and now physical and mental exhaustion. The vast majority of our friends and neighbours have fallen victim to the dreaded disease, and we recognise and have tremendous sympathy with the trauma that they have lived through. But now, at least, they know exactly where they stand, and have a little time to think about their future.

We are still [in May 2001] in a nightmare. We have been subject to every other day veterinary inspections for most of the three months. We now find ourselves in the position of having had no income since the outbreak began. We have no savings to fall back on, as we have spent the last 25 years paying off the mortgage on the farm. My husband works on average 100 hours a week, and often over 20 hours every day but we are now almost bankrupt. The bank rang again yesterday wanting to know how and when we were going to put things right, but we have no answers. I have constantly been phoning all the help line numbers that have been given, seeking information and advice, but no one has the knowledge or the power to help me.

Our small farm now stands alone, surrounded by almost 7,000 empty acres, devoid of any sheep or cattle. Although we have managed to survive, we feel very much as though we have not only been fighting this dreadful disease but battling against our Government. We are the forgotten people. We struggle on, but really wonder why. We have no money, an ever increasing overdraft, stock that no one wants, and very little optimism for the future.

Mr and Mrs Johns, Sheepwash

• • • • •

I write as Church of England parish priest in charge of seven rural parishes, three of which were directly affected by the disease. I think that what has concerned me most as an onlooker is the way in which the outbreaks have led to a rapid breakdown in relationships between farmers and "the Ministry". The common enemy has not been the disease but the Ministry, its apparatus, and officials. This suggests to me that the disease has been the catalyst for something which was developing over time. The opprobrium heaped on the Ministry has not been wholly deserved but (I guess) largely so.

Rev Dr Jones, Bishops Nympton

• • • • •

Quicke's are traditional farmhouse cheese makers, making about 400t mainly traditional cheddar from our own and neighbours' milk. Cheese is stored for around one year on farm before sale. The cow dairy is across a concrete roadway from the cheese dairy enabling milk to be pumped without use of a vehicle. Whey is fed to pigs on site. Cheese is stored in specialist buildings or buildings converted out of farm use, in close proximity to farming activities.

In April 1999, as part of our routine risk assessment, I became concerned about the risk of Foot and Mouth Disease to our business. I asked our insurer to quote us for business interruption from destruction of cheese stocks from Foot and Mouth Disease. They found great difficulty in placing this insurance at Lloyds as no one had asked for it before.

In May 2000, I received a request from a Ministry vet, who visited with a MAFF veterinary adviser who was drawing up MAFF contingency plans for Foot and Mouth. I walked her round our site to establish whether our cheese would be at risk if we were to become infected. She stated that in her view, the cheese was in sufficient close proximity (i.e. less than 200 metres from the animals) that it would be considered a risk, not on the grounds of its containing Foot and Mouth, but that the Foot and Mouth virus might stick to the rind and so get taken out of the farm.

I asked what treatment (if any) would be acceptable to allow a licence to sell rather than destroy. It was her view that the cheese would be destroyed to be on the safe side but she promised to look into it. I chased her up at monthly intervals on the telephone, and with a letter on the 25th September; she replied on the 5th October 2000 saying she would pass it on to Pirbright.

In December 2000 I received a reply from the Deputy Head of Veterinary Exotic Diseases Team at MAFF; his reply, so far removed in time from my original request, failed to answer the question. I spoke with him on the phone in January 2001; he was unaware of which disinfectants were permitted, and whether cheese would be fit to eat after use. He promised to send me the relevant MAFF order.

I contacted MAFF on the 5th February 2001 about insurance for cheese in the event of a Foot and Mouth outbreak, as I had read there was a Working Party on the subject. Uniquely I received a reply in ten days from MAFF who forwarded my letter to a commercial consultant preparing research for the Working Party. I spoke with him almost immediately. The letter was also forwarded for someone to give me details of disinfectants. They replied on the 26th March 2001 (into the Foot and Mouth Disease outbreak) again losing the point - they were telling me how disinfectants are approved, not which ones. I replied, asking for clarification on the fate of cheese.

By this time, many cheesemakers around the country had been told by LVOs that their cheese would be destroyed in the event of infections. Many of us, at considerable cost, moved cheese off farm. Our own cheese director suffered a fatal heart attack in May, brought on in part in my view by the extreme anxiety caused by the threat to his life's work.

M Quicke, Newton St Cyres

. . . . .

I am a development worker for the Pre-School Learning Alliance in the Tavistock and Okehampton areas. During the outbreak I was unable to visit pre-schools, playgroups etc., due to their very rural locations. Many of the pre-schools were affected as their children could not travel off farms etc. Several pre-schools closed for up to six weeks due to staff or families who attend living on farms or because of their location close to farmland. Many groups were unable to fund-raise or hold social events or trips for the children. Morale was very low in both adults and children. Children were aware of the slaughter of animals and even acted it out in their play.

Ms Calvert, Lydford

. . . . .

My neighbour rang me on Sunday, the 14th May 2001 to say he had got Foot and Mouth. Our land was contiguous with his but we did not worry too much as we had not put any stock on this block of land. I rang MAFF on Monday, Tuesday and Wednesday of that week as we were ditching and fencing. They assured me that I could continue to work there (we did not go near the place!).

Wednesday evening about 10 pm another neighbour rang me to ask if I knew we had a dead bullock on our land with a plastic bag on its head. After a lot of enquiries it appears the animal was shot on Tuesday am. A vet who I spoke to on Wednesday pm rang Thursday a.m. to say that the animal was being removed that day. Eventually picked up Friday pm I then queried with MAFF working and stocking possibilities. They told me I could do what I wished.

Mr Bavin, East Anstey

I advertise Bed and Breakfast in the Women's Institute Monthly Magazine "Home and Country". We live overlooking Torbay and part of my advert states "adjacent Coastal Path" which we are. So far, for six monthly insertions, I have had four enquiries and two bookings only, just disastrous.

Mrs Burton, Paignton

. . . . .

On planning issues, the Council was faced with difficulties by the development of the two major disposal sites at Arscott and Ash Moor. Whilst recognising the speed and urgency of the national emergency, the selection processes for these sites ignored the appropriate planning regulations which were required even though the developments were on Crown land. Had the planning process been properly followed, consultation would have been put in place albeit in the very short term which would have enabled the Council to reflect local views which would have led to a comprehensive response.

Mr Brasington, Torridge District Council

. . . . .

The first case of Foot & Mouth disease in Devon was confirmed on 24 February and the last case confirmed on 17 June 2001. Over the intervening 16 week period a total of 174 cases were confirmed and approximately 4,500 premises subject to Form D notices. In the context of the number of cases in England and Wales, Devon lies second only to Cumbria. Primarily concentrated in the north and west of the county, isolated pockets also occurred in the eastern and south western most parts of the county and in Dartmoor National Park. The Infected Area in Devon was lifted on 1 August.

The measures pursued by MAFF to prevent the spread of the disease, in addition to the slaughter of animals and the burning of carcasses on infected premises, included the culling of stock on contiguous premises. Further animals were slaughtered on welfare grounds. This led to a considerable backlog of carcasses awaiting disposal.

At its peak in April almost 200,000 carcasses, primarily sheep, pigs and cattle were reported to be lying on farms, awaiting disposal, with the prospect that this number would increase even further as the contiguous culling programme continued. Many of these carcasses had been there for a considerable period of days and even weeks, with consequent concerns about their decomposition, consequent potential contamination of ground water and risk to public health and amenity, as well as reducing the effectiveness of the culling programme itself.

By the end of April, through recalculation, changes in the extent of the culling programme and through ongoing disposal, the number of residual carcasses in the county was reported to have been reduced to around 25,000, by early May to 5,500; and by late May there was no backlog.

A number of methods of disposal appropriate to the different type of carcass were pursued. These included rendering, incineration, land fill on approved sites, mass burning and mass burial or on-farm burning or burial in accordance with MAFF and Department of Health guidance.

All of the above disposal methods were pursued in Devon, although the potential for on farm burial was removed at a very early stage due to the Environment Agency's concerns about the potential contamination due to the high water table conditions then generally existing in the county. The use of pyres in the County is understood to have ceased on 3 May. DEFRA in June confirmed that there were some 140 small on-farm sites in Devon where carcasses had been burnt. Existing landfill sites at Heathfield near Newton Abbot and Deepmoor, near Torrington, were used for the disposal of animals culled under the contiguous premises and the welfare disposal scheme.

While the greater proportion of carcasses were disposed of 'on-farm' by pyre or in the later stages by rendering or enhanced incineration, at the peak of the crisis MAFF considered that mass disposal and handling sites were required to meet the envisaged backlog of carcasses.

Five such sites were initially promoted but of these only three large facilities at Arscott Farm near Holsworthy, Ashmoor Fields at Meeth and Westlake Farm at Oakford were progressed. Those not pursued were proposals for the burning of carcasses from non-infected premises on sites at Wortham Farm, Lifton and Ellacott Barton, Bratton Clovelly.

Mr Chorlton, Devon County Council

One of the most significant messages and commanding lessons to be learned from the outbreak of the disease in Devon is the importance of the Public Rights of Way network to the economy of the County and the dramatic impact of its closure on the economic and social well being of the County.

The administrative County of Devon has over 4,900 kms of Public Rights of Way within its 409 parishes. This comprises some 6,100 individual paths, of which 3,700 kms (76%) are public footpaths.   1140 kms (23%) are public bridleways and some 60 kms (1%) are byways open to all traffic. In addition to Rights of Way there are a further 800 kms of unsurfaced County roads, bringing the total recreational network for the County to approximately 5,700 kms. (This compares with the Public Rights of Way network in England which extends to 188700 kms (78% public footpaths, 17% public bridleways, 2% byways open to all traffic and 3% restricted byways).

The Devon network includes parts of the South West Coast Path National Trail (300 kms) and regionally important recreational routes including the Tarka Trail and Two Moors Way (total 997 kms including road and permissive sections) which, together with the remaining Public Rights of Way network, are a significant resource for countryside access and for tourism, as has been so dramatically evidenced by the impact of their closure during the current Foot & Mouth outbreak.

On 27th February, three days after the first confirmed case in Devon, the Minister of State for the Ministry of Agriculture, Fisheries and Food, published an Order allowing Local Authorities to close public footpaths and bridleways under 'The Foot & Mouth Disease (Amendment) (England) Order 2001'.

With effect from 28th February 2001 all public footpaths, bridleways and cycleways in the administrative area of the County of Devon, other than those lying wholly within urban areas, were closed and the movement of any person on any such right of way, without lawful authority, prohibited. Contravention of the Declaration constituted an offence under the Animal Health Act 1981 and any person found guilty of such an offence was liable to a fine of up to £5,000.

The closure of the Public Rights of Way network and the perceived message 'the countryside is closed' had a dramatic adverse impact on tourism and the rural economy in Devon. The report commissioned by the County Council from the Agricultural Economics Unit of the University of Exeter (which assessed the position as of 19th March 2001) estimated that over the next 12 months 8700 jobs could be lost in the tourism sector and allied businesses. The reduction in income was estimated as £196m in the tourism sector.

A second part of the study commissioned from the Agricultural Economics Unit was to establish empirical evidence of the loss of business and the extent of jobs being lost in the accommodation sector. The upshot is that of those accommodation providers that responded to the questionnaire, 914 jobs had been lost already by early April 2001.

The economic impact has since been updated and the estimates of income lost and potential job losses revised in the light of events since the previous report and with the benefit of further survey material which has become available. The Devon Recovery Plan, published in July, estimates the potential loss of income to Devon through tourism spending to be £107.5m and the loss of jobs in tourism, 3,332.

Mr Chorlton, Devon County Council

• • • • •

I am a registered blind charity worker, now celebrating my thirtieth year in charity work. Since Friday 30th March 2001, I have generated £12,505.76p for the Green Wellie Campaign over 48 collections and exhibiting at the Honiton Show, this year's Devon County Show, and at the Royal Cornwall Show.

Mr Bond, Lympstone

• • • • •

In the West Country, principally in Devon, twelve members of staff (out of thirty) were dealing solely with FMD-related welfare problems at the height of the crisis. One member of staff was engaged full time in running our brokerage scheme to ensure supplies of feed and bedding to farmers in need. It is estimated that we have devoted over 5,000 men hours to dealing with this crisis.

The RSPCA helped over 750 farmers with licence applications and supplies of feed and bedding, and gave support and advice to many more by telephone. The RSPCA supplied 62,000 bales of hay, straw and silage; 112

tons of feed; and ten lorry loads of woodchips for bedding. Over 103,000 animals benefited from this operation.

Regional Superintendent Tressider, RSPCA

• • • • •

It was established early on that to control the outbreak, without vaccination, livestock suspected of having Foot and Mouth Disease should be culled within 24 hours and contiguous stock within 48 hours. A case was confirmed in North Devon on Thursday 22nd March. The stock was culled 3 days later, Sunday 25th March. The neighbouring farmer was told on Saturday (as he had expected) that his 1,400 breeding ewes plus lambs would be culled. This stock was eventually slaughtered 11 days after the original outbreak, on Monday 2nd April, but only after much pleading to have the cull carried out on welfare grounds. At this point it was confirmed that these animals had now developed Foot and Mouth Disease.

Stock on another contiguous farm was confirmed positive on Wednesday 4th April, 13 days after the original outbreak. Stock on yet another farm, also adjoining the original source, was still running around the fields, 14 days after the initial outbreak. Following this outbreak, three local farms, previously unaffected, were confirmed with Foot and Mouth Disease on the 7th April, the 10th April and the 14th April. We are convinced that if the contiguous cull had not been delayed for eleven days, those new cases above and the cull of contiguous farms including our own could have been avoided.

Mr and Ms Thomas, Muddiford

• • • • •

Although a small community, we have approximately 30 small businesses (not including accommodation providers). Our local shop, garage and pub were badly affected. The garage and convenience store suffered a considerable loss of income and was forced to lay off staff and reduce opening hours. The visitors have not come back. Our local farrier has been badly affected with work almost completely drying up with no trekking and hunting. There has only been a minimal recovery now that bridleways are open. There are fewer visitors riding but there is no hunting.

With businesses looking to make savings where they can, casual cleaning staff were not employed, waitresses not engaged, garden maintenance reduced to a minimum, odd jobs deferred, painting and decorating delayed, and improvements cancelled. This stopped the usual flow of the local economy, which effectively distributed the money brought into the area by visitors from elsewhere into many local pockets. Everyone has suffered.

With Foot and Mouth Disease having such a profound effect on every aspect of the rural community, the confidence of local businesses has suffered. They are less likely to expand, less likely to risk a planned venture, less willing to weather the hard times and increasingly less able to withstand the hard knocks. The consequences of this outbreak of Foot and Mouth Disease will still be felt for some years to come.

Cutcombe Parish Council, Somerset

• • • • •

This parish (9 miles x 4 miles in size) had three actual cases of Foot and Mouth Disease, a great deal of contiguous culling and was completely covered by 'D' notices. The population of approximately 500 people is located in various small settlements and isolated farms/houses. There is one restaurant, tea rooms at Roadford reservoir, a school, three chapels, one church and various holiday lets. There is no pub, shop or post office.

Good things: There was clear evidence of the 'wartime spirit' as the barriers went up and the neighbours rallied round. The telephones were in constant use as people sought to bolster spirits, keep in contact and find out the latest news. This lasted for many weeks until the position clarified and ad hoc survival arrangements were formalised. The sense of community was tested and not found wanting.

Mr Hannaford, Broadwoodwidger Parish Council

• • • • •

Our tiny parish has several small farms, but one large dairy farm of around 100 cows and 50 or so sheep. The parish pulled together to be protective of it. For some time all movements of people outside the parish seemed voluntarily restricted. People did not gather together. Everyone tried to support the farmers. The village hall closed for several weeks. The church lost income as it closed for twelve weeks (it shares an entrance with the dairy farm), pastoral visiting was restricted and there could be no fund-raising events. We had no library van for 4 – 5 months. Depending on the wind, we smelt and saw smoking pyres from all directions but especially the ones two weeks after Easter. The smoke was appalling. Mercifully our parish cows and sheep were not affected. We had no Parish Council meetings for three months. Communication was by telephone.

Mrs Littlewood, Nymet Rowland Parish Council/St Bartholomew's Church, Nymet Rowland

• • • • •

Mrs M. telephones me to ask me what will happen to her sheep which are in a field over the road from a FMD case nearby. Whilst we are discussing the risk etc., to her pet sheep, MAFF are shooting free range bullocks and they have gone mad breaking through the hedges and charging through other stock in their fear.

Three weeks after Mr C. applied for a licence to slaughter his very distressed fat lambs, stranded in a mud field full of swedes and swimming on their bellies in mud, the licence arrives – the day after all his stock had been killed as a contiguous holding.

Ms Vere, Morchard Bishop

• • • • •

Our horse riding on Dartmoor business was closed down due to the restrictions imposed to control Foot and Mouth Disease in the Dartmoor area. We were severely affected by the Foot and Mouth Disease but we are now well on the road to recovery partly due to the efforts of the Regional Development Agency. Our trading figures for July and August were the same as last year if not better which could have been partly due to the marketing efforts of the Regional Development Agency (plus our own efforts of course). Also we have just been awarded the full £15,000 grant from the RDA and we have found this grant reasonably simple to apply for.

Mr and Mrs Newbolt-Young, Widecombe-in-the-Moor

• • • • •

Our business was affected in that it was ended by the cull of our herd. After fighting the contiguous cull for 21 days, we were eventually beaten when MAFF sited a huge mass super pyre on an individual field adjacent to my farm, the wider of implications of which led to the cull of my herd.

Living in a parish completely devastated by Foot and Mouth with only, I believe, one farm left stocked, we were well in the midst of things, but had mistakenly concentrated on fighting the disease and the largely irrelevant contiguous cull, never expecting MAFF's own pyre building actions to result in the loss of our herd.

Mr Easterbrook, Bridestowe

• • • • •

On 17th April , we had an inspection by a Ministry vet, who had come from Petrockstowe. She picked out one lame ewe, examined it closely, breathing into its mouth. Two weeks later on 1st May we were confirmed with Foot and Mouth Disease. One sheep was affected - the same sheep which had been examined by the Ministry vet. Some coincidence out of 1200 sheep and lambs. After confirmation of FMD, the army, police and most officials were considerate and meticulous about cleansing.

D and L Joslin, St Giles in the Wood

• • • • •

The impact of Foot and Mouth on the South West's tourism industry began towards the end of February and accelerated through March and into April. The complete closure of many of the region's assets meant that all sectors of tourism suffered, albeit some suffered more than others, i.e. Farm Tourism, the Moors, Devon and the Forest of Dean.

This resulted in an average of 30% reduction in tourism bookings for March and more worryingly, a significant reduction in forward bookings for May, June and early July. The loss of business in the South West has been calculated at £50m - £60m in March, together with a further £75m lost business in April.

The recovery commenced in May, but the losses continued to mount despite July and August having been relatively buoyant on the coast. It will not make up for the lost earnings earlier in the year. The total loss of business over the year is difficult to calculate but is likely to be in the range of £200m - £300m in the South West. The total impact is calculated by looking at the proportion of South West's tourism sector based on rural farm and moorland tourism (£2.3 billion per year).

Mr Bell, South West Tourism

· · · · ·

People on the sharp end (i.e. vets and farmers) were held back from making decisions on the ground. Although on my first suspicion the heifer did not have the typical symptoms, temperature and foot lesions, after a short time both myself and the vet were 99% sure we had Foot and Mouth Disease but the vet had to obtain permission from London to carry out skin samples which then had to be sent for analysis before confirmation was received 30 hours later. The result of this hold-up was that the cattle were not slaughtered until nearly 60 hours from the first suspicion. During this time we went from one animal showing symptoms and shedding virus at the beginning to 100 animals showing symptoms and shedding virus when they came to slaughter.

When our cattle were slaughtered on 22nd March, there were so many new cases of Foot and Mouth Disease in the County that the vets and slaughter teams could not keep up. It was on this day that the Government made at least three decisions on how to treat farms surrounding the infected premises in as many hours. Having told our neighbours we had been confirmed with Foot and Mouth Disease, imagine how they were feeling when a decision was made that would affect them and then an hour later a different decision was made. The final decision was to cull contiguous animals with very little give on the rules regardless of local knowledge or individual situations. This contiguous cull would result in every farm that was infected with FMD having on average six contiguous farms to be culled at the same time. Our animals were all housed, with our nearest contiguous neighbours at least half a mile away. Our neighbour's sheep, less than a quarter of a mile away that we could see, had woodland in the valley in between and therefore did not count as being contiguous.

The slaughter, building of the pyre and eventual burning of the carcasses were carried out professionally, carefully and compassionately, as quickly as circumstances would allow, but, after the pyre was lit seven days from the first day of suspicion, everybody seemed to disappear and we were left not knowing what to do next. We had an infected premises to clean, no one to tell us what to do and nothing stopping the people coming on or off the farm apart from the signs at the farm entrance.

After three weeks of having no instructions as to what to do, we then had three people in as many weeks who all said they were overseeing a clean-up on our farm but they all seemed to have a different set of directions on what had to be done or interpreted these directions differently. There was no continuity from one farm to another as to what should be done.

Mr and Mrs Webber, Chulmleigh

· · · · ·

I milked on the morning of 20th March. I had no reason to think the day would turn out as it did, but as the last few cows came into the parlour at 7.30, I had my suspicions that we may have a problem. A young cow was later coming in than usual and I saw she had sores on the back of both hind feet. I carried on and milked her and she ate her feed with no problem. On getting the cow into the crush I found she had a large sore on her nose with loose skin hanging off the side of it. On looking in her mouth I found a small sore about half an inch across on the top of her gum. I felt that these symptoms were worrying enough to ring my vet and sound him out.

We both thought it would be wise to play on the side of caution and ring MAFF to get them to come and look. My vet did this, while I went back for another look at the rest of the cows. There's one old character here called Baby, she's always the last to get off her cubicle for milking and enjoys a good scratch on her head to the point that she's a pain to get moving sometimes. She was the first cow I noticed when I went back, she was drooling and flicking her tongue in and out of her mouth. I caught her by the nose there in the yard and put my hand in her mouth to ease her tongue out to see if there were any blisters. To my dismay the skin on most of the top of her tongue came away in my hand. At this point in my mind I realised we had Foot and Mouth.

Mr Webber, Chulmleigh

As engineers and smiths (a small business), the majority of our customers are farmers who did not come in for new work or repairs to be done. Some wanted to stay on their farms as much as possible, others felt they could not afford to spend money and some (a few) still came in for urgent work but did not pay. We found ourselves in the situation for the first time ever of not to be able to pay our VAT. My son also could not go for his usual extra tuition as his tutor lives on a small holding and we have close contact with the farm areas.

On a personal level, my father died and was farming at the time. My mother could not sell the animals and, being elderly, could not take care of them physically or financially. The only path open to her was the animal welfare programme which caused a lot of upset and disagreements amongst the family as no one was in a position to help out on the farm for any length of time.

Mr Bramston, North Tawton

• • • • •

At a Committee meeting of the Residents' Association on the 26th September 2001 the comments on Foot and Mouth Disease were mainly on its effect on prices of food - meat, poultry - in certain retailers. A specific example was a roast chicken which increased from £1.99 to £2.99 in three days.

Mr Shapter, Exmouth

• • • • •

On 4th April a neighbouring farm was confirmed with Foot and Mouth Disease. We are separated from this holding by a large fir plantation (125 acres approx.) and also approximately a 40 acre block of land.

We reluctantly agreed that the cows had to go, although at the time we like most others were ignorant of the legal position concerning the slaughter of healthy stock which is fairly well known now to most people.

The worst thing of all was the way we were all treated by some of the staff at the Ministry offices with their dictatorial and abrupt manner.

T and C Baldwin, Meshaw

• • • • •

We were culled simply because we had animals outside within a 3 km ring of one single Foot and Mouth outbreak. We were not adjoining the outbreak. Vets had been inspecting our animals regularly and all were healthy. They were killed 13 days after the single Foot and Mouth outbreak was confirmed. This caused untold misery not only to us but to everyone around us. Before our animals were killed we were treated in a most inhumane way. We were emotionally blackmailed: "If we got Foot and Mouth, we would give it to our neighbours, and how would we feel then?"

We were told that the animals would be taken away and rendered the day that they were killed but that didn't happen. A pyre had to be built and the ashes were buried. Five months later the ashes had to be removed because they were too close to our water supply. They knew where the water supply was when they started. Nothing that would make things easier for *us* happened.

There was a constant change of people at Exeter and a constant change of rules. This led to unbelievable pressure because we never knew where we were or what we could do. I spent many days over the past six months waiting for someone to phone me back. They very rarely did.

Mrs Mudge, Huccaby

• • • • •

This school was deeply affected by the outbreak of Foot and Mouth Disease, both physically and emotionally. The school closed for one week at the end of February in order to let the initial feelings of panic subside, to give us the opportunity to further assess the situation and to show support for the local community. We reopened when the first pyres were lit and have remained open every since. We would like to pay tribute to the school staff for their care of the children and the professional approach they showed towards the situation.

We feel that the Local Education Authority served the school poorly. When Foot and Mouth was first reported on the Sunday 25th February 2001 there was no one for the headteacher to contact in order to clarify the situation. There was very limited information available on the Internet that related to schools, and specifically to schools in the area immediately around the outbreak. The headteacher was at the school throughout the closure period. The only contact with officers of the LEA was a conversation about disinfectant and the advice given was ultimately proved to be wrong.

Ours is a small rural village and the school is in the centre of it. Many people travel to and pass the school several times a day. We did not want to feel that we were in any way responsible for the spreading of this dreadful disease.

Mr Raven, Black Torrington Primary School

● ● ● ● ●

I am a contract sheep shearer and I lost about £7,000 - £8,000 plus I had to buy a trailer (£1,000) and hire a generator at £50 a week because sheep had to be shorn in the field and no-one was able to move them.

Mr Herniman, St Giles in the Wood

● ● ● ● ●

The emotional impact was very significant being on a farm or a neighbour of a farm where all your animals have been slaughtered on your door step, literally in some cases. Living on a farm 24 hours a day with parents who were stressed fearing for their future was very difficult for young people. There had also been a considerable impact upon those young people who were living near a funeral pyre.

Isolation was the next issue. Rural young people find this to be a big issue for them in normal times but Foot and Mouth Disease made this many times worse. Farmers were so terrified of getting the disease that they barricaded themselves and their families in for several weeks. Even when the initial fear subsided, young people were allowed back to school but they were not allowed out in the evenings. Some were actually sent away to stay with relatives until the foot and mouth disease subsided.

The secretary of one Young Farmers Club rang me to talk through if it would be okay if they could arrange a meeting in a local pub because she felt it was important that the club members got back together. All but one of these members who are involved in farming in any way (about 25) had lost their stock and they felt that they needed to meet as a matter of urgency.

Young Farmers Clubs are often the only social life for rural young people and all 39 of our clubs and the county programmes were suspended on the 25th February. The first social event was on the 2nd August, meaning more than five months without access to their normal social outlets.

Mr Goodman, Devon Federation of Young Farmers Clubs

● ● ● ● ●

It is widely assumed by many that the influence of the church plays little part in the make-up of the community today. I use the example of a fairly typical village to demonstrate that this is not necessarily so. This village is a community of about 540 adults. About half of the population live within the village bounds, the rest on farms. It has a post office/stores, a school and an inn. There is a Parish Church and a Methodist Chapel. Regular attendance at Sunday worship is about forty in total, spread fairly evenly between the two churches.

Special occasions will bring a congregation of up to 150. Even this is only about 30% of the adult population. There is however a strong tradition within local families that certain family members represent the family - "Mother goes for us!". When it comes to funerals the real roots still show. There are few farms where the vicar or the minister is not welcomed with traditional hospitality which gives the Church a unique role still in fostering pastoral care and counselling those in need.

The ordained clergy are spread very thinly indeed over the area. Many will have seven or more churches in their care and the pastoral work tends to overwhelm those in full-time ministry. The Methodist district has appointed a local farmer as a part-time rural worker. During the height of the Foot and Mouth epidemic he was in touch with 80 farming families, listening to their troubles and giving them support.

After the first shock had worn off, the initial reaction of virtually every farmer was to isolate themselves from the rest of the world in every possible physical way. For some this was to remain their position for the next five months. There are a few who even now will not allow any visitors on the farm, and most are still wary of people on non-essential business.

This sense of extreme isolation has been the most crippling psychological effect of the crisis, enhancing as it did the natural sense of isolation experienced on any farm, and the natural concern felt by all that they did not want to be the cause of an outbreak on a neighbour's farm. This concern was reflected throughout the whole community. No-one felt at ease even walking on the roads.

Once the funeral pyres were lit and when the stench of rotting carcasses became common place, the trauma increased dramatically for everyone. It is difficult to explain the sense of desperation felt by all. It was most clearly recognised when one took a trip outside the FMD Exclusion Zone. Even in Okehampton, not affected in the early days of the crisis, life seemed utterly different - people there talked about Foot and Mouth, but not to the exclusion of everything else. Life within the Exclusion Zone became almost surreal, as though there was a physical barrier between us and the rest of the world. All non-essential work came to a halt and many farmers and their families spent hours on the phone supporting each other. Those who were not affected directly by the disease seemed as traumatised as those who were.

Rev Peak, Plymouth and Exeter District, Methodist Church

• • • • •

This rural parish was badly affected by the Foot and Mouth outbreak. It has an electoral roll of approximately 220. Its economy is almost entirely agricultural and based on animal husbandry. There were two cases of Foot and Mouth in the parish that resulted in the majority of animals in the parish being slaughtered (infected, contiguous, and dangerous-contact culls).

The Parish Council feels the whole outbreak was handled badly. There is much anecdotal evidence in the parish about the inept handling of the outbreak. However only facts known to us will be listed here. [These include:]

• A flock of sheep was slaughtered near the Parish Hall. One lamb escaped the cull and was left wandering aimlessly amongst the carcasses for several days.

• The slaughtered animals were piled in a field gateway near the Parish Hall alongside the road, and left rotting for ten days in hot weather. The army eventually agreed to expedite the removal of the carcasses and they were removed one day later. Initially, the lorries that came were inappropriate to deal with the carcasses and different lorries had to be sent.

• After a slaughter of infected cattle (disease detected in cattle on a Sunday, animals slaughtered on a Monday), sheep with lambs at foot were allowed to graze on the infected farm until Thursday, i.e. were not killed for four days after the disease was detected.

• The atmospheric pollution from surrounding pyres was horrendous and the smells were almost unbearable at times.

We would like to point out that the Parish Hall had all functions cancelled for a period of six months and all income was lost. The only major employer in the Parish (grass dryers and feed mills) has now closed with the loss of some twenty jobs. Ancillary workers in the agricultural industry, i.e. contractors, lost all income during the outbreak but achieved some income by working for MAFF during the clean-up of farms.

Mr Penning, Bratton Clovelly Parish Council

• • • • •

I am attaching a list of members who have contacted us [as having been affected by Foot and Mouth]. They are all micro businesses, i.e. either sole traders or employing less than five staff. Whilst it may seem hard to understand how some of these traders could be affected by this crisis, it is amazing how far reaching the effects have been.

Internet Guides; Hotel; Shoe Shop; Small Holding; Cafe; Adventure Holidays; Photographic Supplies; Furniture Creams and Polishes; Public House; Bed and Breakfast; Off Road Driving and Training Centre; Rare Breed Farm; Textile Manufacturer; Supplier of Hams and Delicatessen Goods; Plant Nursery; Ostrich Farm; Gift Shop; Plant Hire Business; Antique Shop; Suppliers of Agricultural Buildings; Picture Framing; Abattoir and Butchers Shop; TV Repairs; Florist; Supplier of Milking Parlour Equipment; Sporting Agency (selling guns and other field sports equipment); Hotel Chalets; Chandlery; Ice Cream Manufacturer; Food Service Company (supplying the catering trade); Fishing Tackle Suppliers; Caravan and Camping Park; Pharmacy; Pottery.

Ms Pring, Devon Regional Office, Federation of Small Businesses

It became known to police officers that many in the farming community were now suffering from various levels of stress because of the crisis. Many police officers acted as unofficial counsellors and some became the only source of contact with the outside world for some isolated in the rural parts of the County of Devon. Sadly, it became necessary to review the policy on the seizure of some of the many firearms to be found in the rural community. This policy arose from an instance in which the police had become involved where some were so distressed they had spoken of taking their own lives. A case by case approach was adopted for firearms to be seized in cases where it was justified. Fortunately, the number of firearms seized was small.

Devon and Cornwall Constabulary

. . . . .

As a News Provider with seven popular services in the County, my team of thirteen journalists have concluded that the performance of MAFF was lamentable - officers were evasive, unhelpful and, in our opinion, the organisation lacked co-ordination and professionalism. We often found that the NFU was the most helpful source of information.

Mr Gilbert, Great Western Radio

. . . . .

The Environment Agency implemented its National Incident Management procedure and opened the Devon Area Incident room on the 2nd March 2001. Our Incident Management procedure includes a National Base Controller, Regional Base Controller and Area Base Controller.

At the height of the epidemic we committed some 40 staff to the Foot and Mouth outbreak in Devon at a total cost, including non-staff, of £0.5m.

By the end of April with rendering at full capacity, public health concerns relating to pyres and an estimated 170,000 carcasses awaiting disposal, considerable pressure was exerted on the Environment Agency to relax the policy for more on-farm burials. However, because of the high ground water levels in Devon and the need to protect groundwater and private water supplies, very few burials could be approved. Much of Devon was waterlogged following the wettest winter for generations, which precluded burial on many farms due to the risk of contaminating ground and surface water and private drinking water supplies.

During the Foot and Mouth outbreak a total of 43 pollution incidents were recorded as a direct result of Foot and Mouth activities on our National Incident Reporting System. A breakdown of each category is:

Pollution Category 1   -   1 incident
Pollution Category 2   -   1 incident
Pollution Category 3 and 4   -   41 incidents

The Category 1 incident was due to the occupant being unable to empty a slurry tank due to premises being within the infected area.   This incident had a significant impact killing 350 brown trout plus salmon, common lamprey, eel, loach and bullhead fish.

Mr Bateman, Devon Area, Environment Agency

. . . . .

Naturally the majority of news' crews from the international, national and regional media immediately beat a path to Highampton and Hatherleigh, the epicentre of the outbreak. With such an intense concentration of effort in this one area, it would have seemed sensible to arrange some sort of media liaison on site. Instead, all calls were directed to MAFF in Exeter. It would have saved a great deal of MAFF's time and ours, if a person on location were given the job of relaying accurate, up-to-date information on the progress of the crisis and the work continuing beyond the barricades.

As the crisis progressed, it became clear that the media's attempts to keep the public informed were regarded as an irritant to MAFF rather than a useful way of disseminating accurate and helpful information.   With so many farmers prisoners in their own homes, the use of the media to inform and assist them was an underused opportunity.

MAFF's press officers in Exeter and London frequently gave conflicting information. There was a period of several days when their total figures for the spread of the disease in Devon did not even tally. Frequently it could take half an hour of consistent telephone calls to actually get through to the Exeter office to get simple statistical information.

The NFU was a key player for the media in finding out what was going on. It could accurately represent the views of farmers - who were calling it seeking information and clarification - and also interpret policy decisions made by MAFF. The role of informed spokespersons fell by default to the Regional NFU. Anthony Gibson and Ian Johnston presented a human, caring and informed view to the public via the media. They made themselves available at all times and consequently will be remembered by many as the heroes of the crisis.

Although Devon County Council did not necessarily play a daily role in our coverage, it did play an important one. The crisis gave the County Council an eagerly grasped opportunity to show itself as a community leader and a voice for the South West's worst affected area in making representations to Government. This community leadership role had been shown before, e.g. over the closure of rural post offices, but it came to the fore during the Foot and Mouth crisis and provided us with new lines to take the story on. Communications with the County Council did not always run smoothly.

Mr Foreman, Carlton TV

· · · · ·

The policy of disposing of carcasses by incinerating them on open-air pyres appears to have been adopted almost by default. It was in MAFF contingency plans, but only as second best to on-farm burial. However, this latter was never likely to be feasible in more than a handful of cases in saturated West and North Devon, and the Environment Agency (understandably enough) regarded it as very much a last resort.

Disposal on open-air pyres therefore became the norm, with disastrous consequences. The logistical difficulties of getting thousands of railway sleepers, hundreds of tonnes of coal and vast quantities of straw to the right place at the right time through a maze of narrow lanes in one of the wettest Springs in recent memory would have daunted the most seasoned and best resourced organisers. It was quite unreasonable to have expected MAFF vets to have been capable of organising such an operation, and the results were predictable.

Even when the military were deployed, the backlog which already existed, coupled with the huge additional demands placed on disposal facilities by the contiguous cull, made for intolerable delays in carcass disposal. Cattle and sheep were left to rot virtually where they had fallen for up to three weeks in the worst cases, with all that that implied for actual pollution of the air, potential pollution of land and water, and almost unbearable living conditions for the farming families concerned and their neighbours.

We cannot say whether the difficulties of arranging disposal also served to delay the slaughter of infected animals, particularly in the early stages of the outbreak, but it cannot have been an incentive to rapid slaughter.

The huge pyres provided images which were irresistible to editors, but which undoubtedly contributed massively to the damage done to Devon's tourism industry. Many farmers believe that it was the pyres that spread the disease. There was certainly evidence of partially burnt carcass material being deposited several miles from the site of a pyre, having presumably been carried there on thermal air currents. And even though there is no evidence that they have caused any lasting environmental damage, the effect which they had on the quality of life and work for people living in their vicinity was devastating.

South West Region, National Farmers' Union

· · · · ·

The Exe Valley fishery has been adversely affected by the Foot and Mouth outbreak. The closure of footpaths has meant that access to the river was denied. The fishery was severely hit over the Easter weekend. It took only £250 when normally it would take £2,500 - £3,000. Over the first four months of the outbreak, the fishery lost £10,000.

Mr Treharne, Countryside Alliance

23 Hunts currently employ a total of 61 people (this does not include volunteers). Two-thirds of these (40) are fulltime members of staff, with the remainder being either part-time, seasonal or casual.

Ten out of the 22 hunts (45%) that responded have laid off staff due to the Foot and Mouth outbreak. A total number of 16 staff have been laid off. In addition one hunt laid off the kennelman for the summer but has taken him back on part-time. Four of the hunts anticipate making redundancies in the future, whilst a further four are not sure whether further redundancies will be made as it depends on the resumption of hunting. In addition, eight of twenty (40%) hunts have cut either the hours or wages of their staff, or are not hiring.

Mr Treharne, Countryside Alliance

• • • • •

On 5th/6th April 112 cows, calves and store cattle and 900 ewes and lambs were contiguously culled. Thirty-seven years of pedigree breeding was lost overnight. The animals were finally burnt five days short of one month after the initial outbreak. This was due to dithering at Exeter and lack of co-ordination which showed itself in many ways [including]:

- Slaughter teams gave half-hour warning that they were coming. They arrived with no equipment to round up or pen the animals.

- No one in authority co-ordinated where the dead animals lay. I had stock from six locations on my pyre, some of which had been left dead for three weeks.

- My sister-in-law had eight phone calls from MAFF to ask the same question, "Have you been culled yet?"

- No one knew how to build a pyre. Mine was too wide and had to be dug twice.

- We waited two weeks to be told the animals were to be taken and watched them rot for ten days. At that time we were being told all contiguous farms were being dealt with within 48 hours.

- A pyre for 112 cattle and 3,500 sheep cost in excess of £120,000. It was poorly constructed so burnt for two and a half months.

Mr May, West Ashford

• • • • •

My business has lost nearly all work over the Foot and Mouth Disease period. We used to employ five full-time workers. At present our small amount of works are sub-contracted with no employees at all. Scheduled replacements for equipment have had to be shelved.

We had six months' work in hand, but at present we have less than two weeks. We are now considering closing the business completely. I personally have not drawn from my business since April 2001 despite working very hard on its recovery. I am not sure where to turn at present.

Mr Jowett, Morwellham

• • • • •

As the disease took hold in the County many Sites of Special Scientific Interest owners were affected, both directly through culls and indirectly through the necessary restrictions placed on movement of cattle. In Devon the total SSSI area (in hectares) in or partly within 3 kilometre FMD buffer zones was 2,303. The number of biological SSSIs within 3 kilometre FMD buffer zones was 28. The number of geological SSSIs within the 3 kilometre FMD buffer zones was 12. There was no direct damage to any of the SSSIs in Devon. Only at Braunton were stock culled on an SSSI.

Mr Collins, Devon Team, English Nature

• • • • •

The whole parish was affected by the need for the slaughter of most animals. The Parish Council feel the consultation with them was minimal. Although notices from the County Council and the District Council were supplied to close footpaths, there was no use of the Parish Council which could have been a valuable source of information to inform local people, through its own networks.

In the Parish there were two large pyres. There were notices put through some doors in the Parish, informing of the imminence of the pyres being lit. There was much rumour and misinformation regarding the danger of the fires, causing concern to a number of people. There was no consultation with the Parish Council whatsoever regarding the pyres.

Bridestowe Parish Council

• • • • •

The Foot and Mouth Disease outbreak led to the cancellation and postponement of many arts activities throughout Devon. Box office receipts and other income fell, sometimes sharply. In several cases this was caused by the reduced numbers of visitors to the area; in others by a reluctance of local people to travel around and risk infection.

It is of course almost impossible to quantify the emotional and social impact of the outbreak. In the arts, there are many examples where events and projects were affected in terms of attendance. In addition the success of those events which did take place was impacted on by the local, regional and national mood during the outbreak period. With village hall events being cancelled one after another, we found one village resolutely determined to continue their long planned village hall music event - determined to show and celebrate community spirit in a time of difficulty.

Mr Humphreys, South West Arts, and Ms Hayes, Devon Arts Forum

• • • • •

One week before Easter this year a MAFF vet turned up on my dairy farm and announced that he had come to carry out a contiguous cull of our herd. All local cases were miles away to my knowledge and so I questioned him. His paperwork showed my farm, my herd address, my holding number and my phone number. At this point I asked him to ring his boss. The answer came back that the "neighbouring farm" was in fact 15 miles away. I was not a contiguous cull - the paperwork was all wrong.

One week later we went down with Foot and Mouth. The only stranger to our farm had been this vet. We had taken extremely careful disinfectant measures. I firmly believe that the MAFF vet brought the infection to our farm and consequently devastated this holding and those of all my neighbours. Once Foot and Mouth was confirmed, the vet sent to us by MAFF was excellent. He handled the awful task of slaughtering the herd with courtesy to myself and staff - and with great consideration of our feelings.

My stockman and I knew every animal. This farm has been in my direct family since the 1930s, and before that was owned by a more distant relative. It can be traced back to the Domesday Book and is the same acreage as it was in 1066AD - with the exception of 50 acres which was given to an uncle in the 1960s.

I was born here, and live here with my father, stepmother, wife and children. My son has just attained a Degree in Agriculture and Business from University and is prepared to carry on. My experience? The trauma and devastation are hard to describe. Silence morning and night - no milking machine. No calves reminding us that they need feeding. Neighbours phoning but not daring to come near.

Our stock were all killed on Good Friday. The initial response handled by the vet was excellent but it soon became clear that communications were not taking place between different parts of the operation. My wife took two calls on the killing day and the following day from MAFF, stating that they were coming to kill the stock. We had only three cats and two dogs left and it was most upsetting. The people on the other end of the phone were most embarrassed when the situation was explained.

We have cleaned and disinfected and found the agent dealing with this to be helpful, although many neighbours have different tales to tell. We are restocking and surviving, but live in fear that it will return. It has taken a toll on us all. Fortunately my son was away at the time and so has returned with the enthusiasm to carry on. He did not see the slaughter or lead the cows to death.

Mr Baker, Umberleigh

Our sheep were destroyed, and our only barn was demolished with no compensation. We both suffered from respiratory problems due to the fires. The C and D process was slow and incompetent. We were unable to work in our studios (as artists) for three months as the electrical supply was cut off by the C and D. We could not leave the farm to work elsewhere. I suffered from depression. The experience of FMD and the subsequent C and D has left us with lasting distrust and lack of respect for Government. We are fearful of the future.

Mrs Vergette, Highampton

· · · · ·

A sheep dealer from Devon had developed and established a large trade in cull sheep and store lambs during the late winter months. The trade involved purchasing sheep from the large markets in Northumberland and Cumbria, and then sorting the sheep into specific marketable groups and reselling them into different markets where their values were marginally more.   Some were delivered directly onto farms, some resold in livestock markets, and some exported for slaughter to countries such as France and Spain.

This trade was well established, had been running for some time and served a useful purpose in that it distributed relatively low value animals in large numbers to places where they were wanted. However, it proved to be a most efficient way of disseminating a highly infectious disease, with the dozen or so infected sheep that were originally taken into Hexham Market being allowed to contact over 60,000 others within the incubation period of the disease, in many parts of the country.   Many of these sheep were returned to the dealer's own home farms in Devon before redistribution, and during their short stay were clipped and sorted, often with the help of other farmers and stockmen in the area, who then returned to their own farms carrying the virus.

Devon is a high stock dense area, containing 165,000 pigs, 1.8 million sheep and 617,000 cattle (DEFRA June census).   Those areas where infection was first seeded are particularly stock dense, and had, perhaps by coincidence, been well used to dealing with TB before FMD came along. The experience gained by TB control may have eased the implementation of the FMD control measures, as the local offices of the State Veterinary Service were reasonably well resourced, with good working relationships with local practices and farms.

The spread of infection from the original index cases in the west of the County towards south and east Devon led to a peak of cases in March.   This reached a maximum of 34 infected premises in the last week of March, leading to the slaughter of 235 holdings in that one week.

Mr Sibley, Witheridge

· · · · ·

We are a farm tourist attraction with over 400 animals to feed and care for. We also have a caravan and camping site and a self catering flat. Due to the Foot and Mouth crisis our business has suffered substantial losses. The business was closed to the general public for nine weeks. Normally two thirds of our animals would have been moved for fresh grazing, but due to the fact that we could not obtain a licence and then we became in an infected area, we could not move animals. Our feed bills rose from £450 per month to £1,200 per month with no money coming in to pay for this extra cost. We did have three camping rallies booked which should have brought us in an extra £3,500 but all these were cancelled by the caravan and camping club.

Mrs Harding, Farway

· · · · ·

The army invited me to demonstrate a design of fire that I claimed would greatly speed up the process of burning carcasses and cut down on the output of atmospheric pollutants. An experimental fire was prepared near Holsworthy in Devon using timber available on the site of a large pyre. The experimental fire measured 8ft by 8ft in area and consisted of a crib of timber baulks (sleepers) 8ft long having a cross section of 9 inches by 5 inches. Two sleepers (bearers), 8ft apart, laid on their broad side formed the base of the crib. A sleeper was laid on its narrow side on both these bearers and the space between them filled with kindling. Over the kindling were placed 12 sleepers laid on their narrow side and spaced equidistantly (about 4 inches) save that the centre 2 sleepers were placed side by side to form a baulk (10 inches by 9 inches).   Eleven more sleepers were laid across the others and placed equidistantly.   Four more sleepers were laid over these, two at the edge and two 2ft from the edge. Pallets were cut to fit between the four sleepers on the top of the crib.

Eight ewes (said to be Suffolk/Mule x) were laid in two rows on their side over these last-mentioned sleepers with the heads of all but one in the centre and three lambs laid over the ewes' heads. Care was taken that the ewe carcasses did not touch each other so that flames could pass around each carcass.

A double layer of pallets was laid over the carcasses and two sheets of 8ft by 4ft particle board laid over the whole to deflect heat and flames onto the top of the pyre intensifying the burning. It was intended that adjustments to the burning rate could be achieved by addition of fuel beneath the crib and between the sleepers. The fire reduced the carcasses to ash in three hours with negligible production of smoke and no smell.

Mr Boyt, Davidstow, Cornwall

· · · · ·

When Foot and Mouth disease broke out in February 2001 we found ourselves at the centre of the Devon outbreak. Within a very short time the disease was confirmed at farms all around us and there was quickly a huge build-up of culled animals in the fields and barns all around us. It was evident that there were not enough labour and facilities available to burn the vast numbers of carcasses, nor indeed to render or bury them.

Reacting to the needs to dispose of large numbers of bodies MAFF took the very reasonable step of looking for a mass burial site. I understand that they surveyed over 30 possible sites in Devon before deciding that Ash Moor was the most suitable. In my opinion MAFF made the right decision at the right time. They completed the purchase of the land very quickly and the original time-span was to be about 10-15 days before filling the pits could commence. At this time there was a desperate need for these pits. From our farm we could see seven or eight pyres burning all round us, the smell was dreadful and was in addition to the smell from the rotting bodies which were steadily increasing in number. One of my neighbours had over 4,000 sheep and 200 cattle destroyed. They laid where they were killed for over a week.

The original MAFF plan was for a private road to be used for access, after upgrading, to the burial pits site. Because of protests, MAFF were forced to build a completely new access road through the clay works entering through the village of Meeth. Building this new road cost several million pounds and caused a delay about 6-8 weeks. By this time the need for the burial pits had passed and we had suffered more pyres and smell, with the resultant trauma. Much of this could have been avoided if the pits had been constructed and put into operation within the original timescale.

Myself and a number of local farmers feel strongly that MAFF did an excellent job in purchasing Ash Moor and planning the construction of the burial pits. I personally commend MAFF for their efforts in relation to the Ash Moor pits and in fact with certain reservations their general handling of the FMD outbreak in Devon. Of course, mistakes were made, but in view of the enormity of the task, I think given their limited resources MAFF did its best.

Mr Banks, Petrockstowe

· · · · ·

We have guest accommodation (6 letting rooms) and 2 self-catering cottages. Between March - May 2001 inclusive business was down some 60% overall. In June and the first 2 weeks in July business picked up with last minute bookings and much repeat business. The end of July and beginning of August was very bad - over 90% down some weeks on 6-year average. Some 85% of our business has been repeat business (up from annual average of 65%). Without this we would have been really struggling.

We have minimised impact on us in 3 ways:

a) deferred virtually all refurbishment plans

b) drastically cut casual staff hours

c) reduced advertising spend for 2002 by approx. 80%

The impact of this on our suppliers and staff is dramatic:

a) builders, electricians, furniture and equipment suppliers have not had the orders they would expect

b) some staff hours have been cut by 80% on previous years

c) membership of West Country Tourism has been lapsed and advertisement in North Devon Guide discontinued

We judge that the media have been major contributors to the crisis in tourism by showing carcasses and pyres nightly. The worst thing is that every time F&M is mentioned - even now - they put out library footage of these scenes. The worst is yet to come. Many businesses will just not have sufficient in their savings to see the winter through.

North Devon District Council were excellent in organising a deferment of the business rates - minimum bureaucracy and speedy solution. The financial support available to businesses ("Meacher money" up to £15k) was slow, confusing and linked into excessive accountancy/consultancy advice. The rules kept changing and the anticipated delays in distributing the funds put us off. All we needed was some fast track assistance for 2002 advertising which needed to be in place by July at a figure based on our previous years.

Mr Jones, Eastleigh

· · · · ·

We run an English Language School for foreign adults and children. We spent a great amount of time on the telephone and email informing and reassuring clients regarding the crisis. Over-information and misinformation from the press and authorities worldwide created a real sense of panic amongst our foreign clients, individuals, travel and educational agents, schools and other educational establishments as well as government authorities.

As a result we had a great number of cancellations, particularly from Junior groups, often as a request from their governmental authorities. Our overall bookings went down by 20 % this year, going down by nearly 800 student weeks.

Our Junior students bookings went down by 30% this year. Our Junior students bookings went down by 53% this summer (over 10 weeks). Our bookings for Junior students in groups went down by 70%. These figures indicate clearly that the group organisers who normally promote in February/March/April just did not bother this year or were very unsuccessful as a direct result of the media coverage regarding Foot & Mouth.

English in Devon, our local association of ARELS (Association of Recognised English Language Services, accredited by the British Council), did write to Business Link regarding recognition of the problem and possible support but did not even get an acknowledgment.

Ms Borgen, Exeter

· · · · ·

This is a large Devon primary school, on the edge of the moors. The effect was profound. All the children were caught up in the atmosphere of despair. Visits and access to local study areas were stopped. Meetings / courses etc were cancelled. One particular colleague had to move off his farm and live apart from his wife in order to attend school. The visual impact in North Devon was very disturbing.

Ms Quiggin, Woodlands Park Primary School, Ivybridge

· · · · ·

The company that I own and manage exports bull semen from AI Companies, Breed Societies and individual breeders across the UK. It is based at my home. We work to strict Health Protocols for each bull that vary from country to country. Having built up the company again after the BSE crisis we were on course to achieve a turnover of £350,000+ in 2001.

We lost all this trade on Day One of FMD as every country that we export to withdrew their Health Protocols and have banned imports until at least 3 months after the last case is reported in the country. 95% of our business has been lost.

Mr Wills, Ilsington

· · · · ·

The children, parents, staff and governors of this primary school have all been touched by the outbreak whether they are involved with the business of farming or not. Only one local farm has not had its stock slaughtered and so the whole area was affected by the stench that ensued from the rotting carcasses and then smoke from the funeral pyres. The school and all businesses have been affected by the destruction of the farming industry in the area and the personal trauma is unquantifiable.

The Devon experience of FMD is ongoing in our area. The effect on the countryside, economy and families has been traumatic and remains so as the threat of FMD returning still looms over farming families in the area. Many of our families, worrying about their livelihood, kept children home initially, until the realisation of the time-scale involved meant serious interruption to their children's education. Sadly, this meant we often had to send children home knowing that their stock was about to be slaughtered.

Clinton School, Merton

• • • • •

We provide English language courses for foreigners and, from March to June, our student numbers were down between 25% and 30% on previous year's figures. We have also suffered a decrease in bookings from September to the end of the year - we usually have 30 students in the school all year round (rising to 90 in the summer) but we are currently working with only 15 students until Xmas.

The cash flow projections are naturally very worrying. We tried to get help from both Plymouth and Exeter Chambers of Commerce but I left messages that were not returned and couldn't get any further, even with the Business Link offices. We need help - we are a small business and we provide employment for local teachers, host families and therapists, as well as attracting foreign students to the town all year round, with the knock-on effect for local high street businesses.

Ms Barker, Totnes

• • • • •

Many farms and small businesses in our parish were affected by restrictions of movement of animals, closure of local markets and slow down of tourists to the area.

The councillors of this Parish Council were very keen to help to protect the boundary points into our parish by disinfecting, and numerous letters and e-mails were sent to the County Council and to MAFF trying to gain permission to carry this out. Devon County Council stated that if MAFF agreed to this as a plan of action they would carry it out. When we telephoned the MAFF helpline, they thought it was a good idea, but according to Devon County Council it was never proposed to them as a plan of action. We did not feel that we could proceed as it required placing materials on the public highway and if an accident should have occurred we, as a parish council, would not be insured.

Mr Badcock, Kings Nympton Parish Council

• • • • •

This Society is 110 years old, is based in Devon, has two full time and one part time member of staff, and records the pedigrees of the South Devon breed of beef cattle. It promotes the breed and its attributes to other farmers across the whole country (there are 600 herds from Penzance to Aberdeen) and abroad. It promotes the meat to the retail sector and recently launched its own marketing scheme to brand the beef in butchers shops up and down the South West. It runs sales for members to sell their top quality livestock. It offers a multitude of membership services including newsletters, journals and technical support.

The Breed Society has seen most income sources severely reduced during the FMD crisis, particularly coming on top of the 5 years of worries caused by BSE. Members are reticent to register pedigrees (the Society's main source of income) when they see little or no prospect of selling breeding cattle. There are no Society Sales for the Society to generate commission and there are no private sales either so transfer fees, from the transfer of pedigrees when sold, are non-existent. There have been no social get-togethers at which fundraising would normally take place and merchandise sales too.

The South Devon breed has had a deep and long lasting effect on the county. It is the breed from which clotted cream came. Its homeland is the South Hams and its beautiful green fields full of red grazing cattle are the direct result of South Devon breeders and their cattle.

In other countries Breed Societies are supported by the government to allow the nation's heritage to thrive, and to promote export sales. This is not the case here and if the crisis were to continue the Society's ability to support its membership and continue its current functions would be severely curtailed to the detriment of its 600 farmer members and the heritage of the County and the country.

L Lewin, South Devon Herd Book Society

We are beef, sheep and dairy farmers who were contiguous on three different sides. We battled with MAFF and won to keep our cattle and sheep through legal action. We were the first farmers to instruct the solicitors, Stephens and Scown.

Mr Westaway, Chulmleigh

· · · · ·

The Devon Guild of Craftsmen is an arts organisation representing some 230 craftspeople from across the South West. The Foot and Mouth epidemic has meant a drop in profits of £30,000 at our Riverside Mill Crafts Centre and an accompanying 10% drop in visitor numbers (up to 30% at the start of the crisis). This loss will seriously affect not only the Centre itself but also our ability to support all of the microbusinesses, ie craftspeople, across Devon who were also directly affected. Some craftspeople in Devon experienced a 70% drop in takings and some have gone out of business.

Mr Murdin, Devon Guild of Craftsmen, Bovey Tracey

· · · · ·

Report from a farm at Burrington

With my family I have been here since 1946, coming with my parents from my grandparents' farm also in the parish. We brought sheep with us as a nucleus for our flock. Although not a pedigree flock, every year the best ewe lambs were selected to replace culled ewes, as had been the practice from grandfather's early days in farming - so bloodlines went back to them.

We saw no reason for this pattern to change until 10th April 2001 when we became another case of Foot and Mouth Disease in Devon. Having been living on a knife-edge for seven weeks - as had every other farmer in Devon and other areas - the shock was still considerable. That day seemed endless yet so much happened swiftly entirely beyond our control.

On 5th April we had heard of a confirmed outbreak in the village, with sorrow and compassion for them and for the local people having to endure the sight and smell of rotting carcasses for days on end.

Beyond our control and a very sad part for us was the inevitable involvement of adjoining neighbours - all are our friends, some for a life-time. By the end of that day we were all devastated, especially our daughter and son-in-law, having helped to slaughter 66 bullocks, 415 ewes, 9 rams, plus more than 600 lambs - lambs I had seen skipping around their mothers when I looked out of the window in the morning, knowing that would be the last time.

The Ministry vets and slaughter team did their jobs as well as they were able, with care and consideration. April 11th dawned a beautiful morning almost insensitively bright for the gruesome sight of piles of dead sheep lying in the fields and yard full of dead bullocks already blown up to bursting point, and the slaughter team coming again to kill all our other daughter's sheep in the afternoon. "Fly", our sheepdog, was very subdued afterwards; she must have thought it strange to keep driving flocks into pens but not away again.

Mornings came and days went by without the need to think of animals being fed, or checked for lameness or looking poorly. We had a silence around us, a dog with no work, hay silage and straw with nothing to feed or bed. There was an overpowering smell everywhere which we had to live with for eighteen days because, although we hoped the animals would be buried, we were only given the choice of a funeral pyre or rendering. Believing that the pyres were a source of spreading the disease, we did not wish to inflict that on further neighbours - and on our conscience.

Since the start of lambing in early January I had been waiting for the day when the kitchen windowsill would be free from bottles, teats, jugs and a box of milk powder to feed orphan lambs. When that day came, how I wished them back again.

We were very comforted by so many phone calls, letters, cards, offers to shop and collect things, and cheering gifts. The box at the end of the lane has become our lifeline while we continued as virtual prisoners here.

Now five months later we are nearing the end of a meticulous cleaning and disinfecting programme of equipment, machinery and large number of older and ancient buildings. Our only income since last November, when we sold the remainder of our year 2000 lambing crop, has been from MAFF/DEFRA for this cleaning. We are still on Form A, so unable to restock and not sure if it is safe to do so at present with Foot and Mouth Disease still active in certain areas. We could not face the trauma of having the disease a second time.

Life in the community has suffered badly, with very little fund raising and social events happening even now. So opportunities to meet together are few. We still avoid visiting anyone with cloven hoofed animals. We meet them in town or at some other venue. We still feel very vulnerable to any comments regarding farmers' actions and movements and understand the problems and distress of those who have retained their flocks and herds and the heavy financial burdens they are still facing.

Life will never be the same for so many. The situation was compounded by the casual manner in which FMD was treated in the first weeks, the callous way in which we were left with dead animals around us for 18 days after slaughter and the many instances of slapdash record keeping in Ministry offices.

Another report from Burrington

From the start of the outbreak there was a total collapse of the social structure within the rural area leading to desperate isolation for many people. There was a cessation of regular village activities: youth club, skittles, council meetings, church services, school fixtures were all cancelled, and children were kept off school. The closure of livestock markets - the regular meeting places for farmers and their suppliers - increased the feelings of isolation and depression felt throughout the community. There is little doubt that these factors contributed to a suicide in this parish. Seven months on and most activities have resumed, but spontaneous visits to farms no longer happen.

The many local businesses closely connected to the rural community faced great uncertainty in the early stages of the outbreak. The fear of unwittingly spreading the disease caused paralysis in the rural economy affecting all businesses from village shops, pubs and hotels through to builders, agricultural suppliers and so on. Time has lessened this paralysis but many rural businesses have had a lean time during this crisis.

The impact on the livestock farmers was immense. Those whose animals were culled experienced the terrible trauma of slaughter and disposal. However those whose animals survived, suffered draconian movement restrictions, resulting in unprecedented animal welfare and financial problems. The routine husbandry of many animals was so disrupted that both animals and farmers suffered greatly.

The chaotic disposal system allowed large numbers of both infected and contiguously culled animals to lie rotting beside public roads and in the centre of our village for up to 17 days. The sight and smell were utterly abhorrent and such a 'medieval' situation must never be allowed to happen again.

Burrington Parish Council

· · · · ·

We breed pedigree Suffolk sheep. Our flock has become extremely successful. Last year we won the title of the champion flock in the Western Area Branch (West of England and Wales) and the West Country through the Suffolk Sheep Societies Flock Competitions.

Our sales season is relatively short beginning mid-July through to early August for the top ram lambs to fellow breeders. 80% of these ram lambs are sold outside of the County. We were still on a 'Form D' and within the last infected area until the end of July, hence these sales were lost. Our top stud ram is in Scotland and the only way of using him was through AI, which was not allowed on our farm until the end of August, meaning these lambs will be born three weeks later than in normal years and also three weeks later than those of our closest competitors at next years sales (if there are any!). We have also lost out on the sale of thirty to forty shearling ewes, which would normally be sold to other breeders throughout Britain.

It is impossible to work out exact losses for the year and indeed for next year, but an estimate would be that 75% of our business has been lost due to the Foot and Mouth outbreak. I never want to see dead livestock lying across Devon's fields for three weeks waiting for removal. I am only extremely lucky that none of them were mine, as neighbours and friends have lost theirs.

Mr Irwin, Kings Nympton

We provide a wide-ranging performing arts and educational development programme involving professional companies, amateur groups and a range of local organisations, particularly educational establishments. The overall impact of FMD has seriously impaired certain aspects of our work and created financial difficulties for the organisation as a whole. Movement was inhibited, and so many community activities had to be curtailed. This resulted in the cancellation of many events, including education, participation and amateur projects.

Our estimate is that £20,000 to £30,000 income was directly lost from reduction in audiences, show cancellations, school movement restrictions and increased marketing and production costs incurred. This has had a direct impact on our growth plans following a period of artistic and financial stabilisation.

Mr Giddings, North Devon Theatres, Barnstaple

• • • • •

The Town Council are owners of much commercial property in Tavistock. The closure of our cattle market has cost us £20,000 in lost rental this financial year, and several retail units have been empty due to the downturn in commercial activity. In all, we are 20% or more short on our expected rents this year due to the FMD restriction. This will affect our programme of works in the town and also have a knock-on effect on the setting of the precept next year. As a local authority we get no rate relief on these matters.

The closure of Whitchurch Down forced all the dog owners for miles around to bring their dogs to our town's open space to be walked. We had to expend resources and money on cleaning up and implementing the dog byelaws, again with no recompense. The unquantified decrease in visitors to the town has affected all the traders.

Tavistock Town Council

• • • • •

This primary school is situated in the middle of an affected area and all the farms in the parish (except one) had their animals slaughtered, resulting in the village being engulfed in smoke etc. from the burning pyres (fortunately for the school this happened at half term and so the school was not forced to close). All pupils, parents, staff and governors were affected by the outbreak which had, and is still having, repercussions throughout the whole district. Governors were initially given very little guidance and, even after receiving guidelines from Devon County Council, there were still many areas where the local community had to support itself.

The proposal to build a mass burial site at Petrockstowe, where children from this school live, had a dramatic effect on the whole community, but especially on some parents of young children. Meetings were held throughout the district and a meeting was held with public health personnel at this school, to inform and educate parents re any potential risks, but, because of the untried nature of the site, many people are still unable to accept that this would not cause harm to the local environment and the health of the community. It is hoped that this site may never be used.

Mrs Crocker, Clinton School, Merton

• • • • •

We are a fallow deer park, located in the disease hot spot of Hatherleigh. We have our own licensed game processing facility, and have set up a producer group where we purchase and market the production from 9 fallow deer parks throughout the Westcountry. We purchase their production, and process it in our facility and then market and sell the processed cuts nationally. We therefore act as the primary outlet for these producers. We pay the producers a premium for quality stock, and thus have their quality product to add to our own production to provide continuity supplying our retail outlets.

Our property is located 1 mile from the initial outbreak in Devon. Our D notice was issued on 22nd March, whereupon, we were prevented using our own production in the food chain. MAFF approved that we could continue trading with our existing or new producers outside D notice areas. Carcasses were picked up from the various parks, brought into our facilities, processed and then taken from our facilities up to London for sale.

We were visited every 2 to 3 days by MAFF vets, who openly admitted that they would have to rely on our knowledge of the natural characteristics of fallow deer to identify symptoms out of the ordinary. Our neighbours were visited every 10 days or so. When enquiring why this difference we were informed that we were a contiguous property. On further investigation, they conceded that this was not the case, the infected property in question being some distance away, with other holdings between ours and theirs.

On no occasion did the same MAFF vets visit both us and our immediate neighbour, each time sending out different teams from Exeter. On one occasion, whilst leaving the house to meet the vets at the end of our drive, a call was received from other vets leaving Exeter to visit us to carry out the same inspection.

Toward the end of the outbreak in Devon, our neighbour's stock was slaughtered on suspicion, due to a lesion being found in one lamb. The vet involved was convinced it was Foot and Mouth. His entire stock of sheep, and dairy cows was slaughtered. My deer herd was grazing in our paddock adjacent to the field. We, being contiguous, were informed that if the tests on the lesion proved positive, our deer would be culled. Two days later one of our 2 remaining sheep was found to have a lesion. The MAFF vet stated that it was definitely not Orf, and so the sheep, and our pet goat were slaughtered, and an A notice served on our farm. Our deer were left pending results of the blood samples from the slaughtered animals. Both our neighbour's and our samples proved negative.

Mr Kent, Hatherleigh

· · · · ·

The lack of communication with the people living in surrounding areas was amazing. The army managed to block both routes from the link road to Roachill at the same time completely ignoring the fact that they were operating at the time of the school buses. Hence a school child was dropped on the road and asked to walk home. She had to walk through the bodies of dead sheep which were being picked up by MAFF men in white suits. The men in the carcass collecting lorry shouted at her to stop, they put her in the lorry cab and radioed for an army pickup to collect her and bring her home another way, but they had blocked the other way with another lorry.

This has happened before elsewhere when a parent due to collect her child off the school bus was allowed to get between two carcass holding lorries. The school bus could not wait for her to arrive and drove off taking the child on a route which it did not know, hence the child had a screaming tantrum on the bus because it was afraid. The poor mother did not know how to get to the child because she was in the car, so she wasn't by her phone and other parents were trying to contact her.

Miss Coffin, South Molton

· · · · ·

Of our 5 Devon Discovery Outdoor and Residential Centres, 3 were majorly affected by FMD. A total of 86 week and weekend residential courses, mainly for Devon school and youth groups, had to be cancelled. These were offset by rearranging 7 courses to other times or locations. Financially, a conservative estimate of loss of income to Devon Discovery for the period to 26th February to 4th October 2001 is £90,159. We also have a concern that a number of groups who found alternative venues not affected by FMD, or simply cancelled their residential course, will not return to our Centres.

Mr Berry, Devon County Council

APPENDIX

Mr G Norris	Bradstone	Mr F Lowry	Beaworthy
Rev P Fitzpatrick	Northmoor Team Ministry, Okehampton	Devon County Council	Mr M Thomasson, County Emergency Planning Officer, Exeter
Dr N Atkinson	Dartmoor National Park Authority, Bovey Tracey	Mr G Powell	Exmouth
Mr T Jones	Devon and Cornwall Business Council, Plymouth	Devon County Council	Mr B Smith, Adviser for Outdoor Education, Exeter
Mrs L Rolls	Princetown	Mr H Richardson	Witheridge
Mr R Holdsworth	Totnes	Mr A Fletcher	Paignton
Mr M Brice	Stoodleigh	Miss G Hall	Okehampton
Mr D Geeves	St Austell, Cornwall	Mrs C Hughes	Branscombe Parish Council
Mrs W Parkhouse	Ivybridge		
Mr G Streeter	Member of Parliament for SW Devon	Mrs P Stone	Chagford Parish Council
		Miss R Roberts	Holne
Mr B Inwood	Christow	Mr R Wright	Great Torrington
Ms L Smith	Devon Association of Parish Councils, Exeter	Mr S Hill	Exmouth
		Mrs R Gethin	Buckland-in-the-Moor
Mr E Haes	Hayle, Cornwall	Mr M Hancox	Stroud, Glos.
Mr P Trainor and Ms C Norman	Barnstaple	Mr B Linfoot	Devon Area, Ramblers' Association, Cullompton
Mr W Willmetts	Knowstone		
Cllr Mrs L Gear	Ilfracombe	Mr S Gibbins	Clyst Hydon
Mr R Gard	Crediton	A & L Gifford	Milton Damerel
Devon County Council	Ms A Dentith, Waste Management Team, Environment Directorate, Exeter	Ms K Lovell	Barnstaple Town Council
		Mr C Moor	Local Government Association, London
Mr M Parsons	Newton Abbot		
Mrs E Brooks	Monkleigh	Mr M Pile	Kentisbury
Mrs P Trumper	Farringdon	Mrs J Ackner	Morebath
Mrs D Parkinson	Feniton	Mrs T Hancocks	Devon Federation of Womens' Institutes, Exeter
C and A Tucker	Crediton		
Ms F Walker	North Tawton Development Trust	Ms J Beer	North Devon NHS Primary Care Trust, Barnstaple
Sir S Waley-Cohen	Simonsbath, Somerset		
Mr R Fieldhouse	Thorverton	Mr C Jewitt	Stoke Hill Beagles, Exeter
Mr M Vaughan			
Staverton Parish Council		Mr M Dymond	Ilfracombe
Mrs J Chave	West Hill	Mr R Baker	Yarnscombe
Mrs D Tappin	Pyworthy	Mr A Griffin	Exeter

Mrs A Crocker	Meeth	Ms J Rudge	Connexions Cornwall and Devon Ltd, Launceston, Cornwall
Miss B Chinneck Scoble	Okehampton		
Mrs R Kittow	Payhembury		
Ms J Russell	Chittlehampton Parish Council	**Uffculme Parish Council**	
		Ms S Burnham	Exeter
Mr J Fowler	Ilfracombe	Dr P Pay	Chulmleigh
Mr G Symons	Shaldon	Mr P Phillips	Hartland
Mr M Jecks	South Zeal	Mr D Incoll	West Devon Borough Council, Tavistock
Mrs J Rudman	High Bickington Church of England Primary School		
		Mr J Brooks	Dunsford
Mr A & Mrs J Cottey	Chittlehampton	Ms R Thomas	South West Forest, Beaworthy
Miss J Lapthorne	Plympton	Mr B Bruins	SW Green Party, Crediton
Mr M Tighe	Great Torrington Town Council		
		Heanton Punchardon Parish Council	
Mr M Moore	Ottery St Mary	Mr & Mrs P Bown	Wembworthy
Mr A & Mrs M Johns	Sheepwash	Mr & Mrs R Wedlake	Chulmleigh
Mr K Jones	Bickington	Mr A Holland	High Bickington
Mr D Meldrum	Chagford	Mrs T Nicholas	Marwood
Rev D Ursell	Dolton	Mr J Graham	Woodleigh
Mrs J Hardy	Buckerell	Mr W Luxton	Petrockstowe
Mr D Tucker	Romansleigh	Ms B Fryer	High Bickington
Rev Dr A Jones	The Oakmoor Ministry, Bishops Nympton	Mrs L McBride	Knowstone
		Mr & Mrs H Barrow	Frithelstock
		Miss G Edsell	Newton Tracey
M Quicke	Newton St Cyres	M & A Marshall	Holsworthy
Ms M Calvert	Lydford	Mrs J Wilson	Sampford Courtenay
Mr K Bavin	East Anstey	Mr J Sellgren	County Councils Network, London
Mr M Leighton	Kilmington		
Mr S Richardson	Western Counties Veterinary Association, Modbury	Mr H Davis	Teignbridge District Council, Newton Abbot
Cllr J Glanvill	Woodbury	Mrs J Willoughby	South Brent Parish Council
Mr J Varley	Clinton Devon Estates, East Budleigh		
		Mrs P Townsend	East Worlington Parish Council
Mr R Head	Devon Farms Accommodation, Oakford	Mr D Woodman	Challacombe
		Mr C Latham	Marwood
Mr A Jackson	Callington, Cornwall	Ms G Douglas-Mann	Petrockstowe
Cllr D Shadrick	Holsworthy	Mr M Tomlinson	Petrockstowe
Mr R Drake	Drewsteignton	Ms C Hutchings	South Devon Tourism Association, North Bovey
J & B Skinner	Meeth		
Mr R Thomson	Tiverton		
Mrs M Jones	Widecombe-in-the-Moor	Mr J Skinner	Meeth
		Ms B Boundy	Tiverton
Mr M Cook	National Trust (Devon Region), Broadclyst	Mrs J Gill	Sourton
		Mr F Payne	Totnes
		Mr J Hawkins	Halwill Parish Council
		Mrs E Phillips	Longdown

Mrs P Kellaway	Bratton Fleming
Mr G Kellaway	Bratton Fleming
Mr K Lancaster	Kennerleigh Parish Meeting
Meeth Parish Council	
Cllr D Key	Upottery
Mr P Evison	Bondleigh
Mrs M Watson	Beaworthy
Mr P Reeve	Clyst St Mary
Mr S Sutcliffe	Broadhempston
Mr J Stanbury	Knowstone
Mr A Beer	Stoke Rivers
Ms R Love	South West Coast Path Team, Exeter
Devon County Council	Mr A Jordan, Home/School Transport Service, Exeter
Mr P Hygate	Botus Fleming, Cornwall
Mrs M Smith	Yarcombe Parish Council
Cllr J Lambert	Kingsteignton
Mr R Easterbrook	Bridestowe
Mr M Elsworthy	Monkleigh
Mr C Dapling	Devon County Council Farm Tenants' Association, Kentisbury
Rev. J Peak	The Methodist Church, Plymouth & Exeter District
Exmoor National Park Authority Dulverton	
Mr D Batchelor	League Against Cruel Sports, London
Mr M Goodman	Devon Federation of Young Farmers Clubs, Exeter
Mrs R Gifford	Hartland
Ms S Bizley	Citizens' Advice Bureau, Okehampton
Miss B Herrod-Taylor	North Tawton
Mr R Herniman	St Giles in the Wood
Mr C Dare	Upottery
R Glanville	Exbourne
Dr J Stoneman	Exbourne with Jacobstowe Parish Council
H Nancekivell	Exbourne
Mr R & Mrs J Phipps	Exbourne
M Brend	Exbourne
Mr M Raven	Black Torrington Church of England Primary School
Mrs R Mudge	Huccaby
T & C Baldwin	Meshaw
Mr P Scott	Friends of the Earth (East North Devon Group), Barnstaple
Miss B Ware	Bow Parish Council
Mr J Shapter	Exmouth Residents' Association
Mr G Thomas	Highampton
Ms P Cather	Abbotskerswell
Mr P Whitehouse	East Ogwell
Mr T Bramston	North Tawton
Mrs P Webber	Chawleigh
Mrs B, Mr R and Mr R Howle	Kingsteignton
A Holmes	Ottery St Mary
Mr A Wright	Sandford
Mr R Deane	Buckland Filleigh
Mr C Paull	Sherwell Parish Council
Mr R Domled	Atherington Parish Council
Mrs N Hawkins	Hatherleigh
Mrs S Bromell	Bideford
D Evans	Lydford Parish Council
Mr J & Ms J Webber	Chulmleigh
Rev. D Ursell	Diocese of Exeter, Rural Convenor, Dolton
Mr P Edwards	Mid Devon District Council, Tiverton
Mr M Bell	South West Tourism, Exeter
Ms C Broom	University of Plymouth, Seale Hayne Faculty, Newton Abbot
D & L Joslin	St Giles in the Wood
Mr S Pitcher	North Devon District Council
Mr N Page-Turner	Luppitt Commons Trustees, Honiton
Ms A Harvey	Blackawton Parish Council
Mr R Easterbrook	Bridestowe
Mr & Mrs R Newbolt-Young	Widecombe-in-the Moor
Ms W Vere	Morchard Bishop

Mrs A Minchin	Axmouth Parish Council	Mrs B MacDonald	Moretonhampstead
Messrs Toller Beattie	Barnstaple	D & P Woods	Family Farmers Association, Aveton Gifford
Mr C and Ms S May	Ashford		
Mr C Watson	Chawleigh	Mrs J Burton	Paignton
Mrs V Littlewood	Nymet Rowland Parish Council and St Bartholomew's Church, Nymet Rowland	Devon County Council	Mr C Lomax, Acting Head of Economic Development, Exeter
		Devon County Council	Ms L Osborne, Devon Library & Information Services, Exeter
Mr A Steen	Member of Parliament for Totnes	Mr C Humphrey and Ms J Hayes	South West Arts and Devon Arts Forum, Exeter
Mrs P Carrington	Buckland Monachorum		
Mr P Wrayford	Kingsteignton	Ms F Winder	Royal Society for the Protection of Birds, Sandy, Bedfordshire
Ms C Stevens	Cutcombe Parish Council, Somerset		
Devon County Council	Mr D Roberts, Land Agent, County Farms Estate, Exeter	Mrs A Browning	Member of Parliament for Tiverton and Honiton
Mr A Hannaford	Broadwoodwidger Parish Council	Anonymous	Yelverton
		Ms A Beech	Stocking Pelham, Herts
Cutcombe Parish Council	Somerset		
Ms C and Mr R Thomas	Muddiford	Bridestowe Parish Council	
Mrs R Newton	Knowstone	Ms J Barrow	South West of England Regional Development Agency, Exeter
Mrs I Riley	Knowstone Parish Council		
Regional Superintendent J Tresidder	RSPCA (Regional Headquarters), Exeter	Mr P Collins	English Nature (Devon Team), Exeter
Mr G. Saunders	Devon Wildlife Trust, Exeter	Mrs S George	Weare Giffard Parish Council
Mrs E Cass	Merrivale	Ms D Somers	Payhembury
Mr J Hammond	Exeter	Mr D Johns	Payhembury
Mr P Bond	Lympstone	Mr B Salter	Hembury Fort, nr Honiton
Devon County Council	Mr E Chorlton, Environment Director, Exeter (interests as Public Rights of Way Authority)	A & S Loud & Sons	Lewdown
		Mr W Turpin	Chawleigh
		Mr J King	Chawleigh
		Mr F Griffiths	Tavistock
Devon County Council	Mr E Chorlton, Environment Director, Exeter (interests as Highway & Local Planning Authority)	Ms V Clements	Exmouth
		Mr M Jowett	Morwellham
		Mrs E Cooper	Dartmouth
		P Mayston	West DEN, Tavistock
Mr T. Brooks	Country Land & Business Association (Devon Branch), Exeter	Mr Martin	Witheridge
		Mr D May	West Ashford
Mr R Brasington	Torridge District Council, Bideford	Mr M Gingell	South Molton Town Council

Ms C Fanconi	Okehampton and District Council for Voluntary Service and Voluntary Bureau, Okehampton
Devon County Council	Ms H Allison, Head of Communications and Information, Exeter
Devon County Council	Mr R Rivett, Head of Trading Standards, Exeter
Devon County Council	Mr L Darling, Transport Co-ordination Service, Exeter
Ms R Bagley	South Hams District Council, Totnes
Mr M Treharne	Countryside Alliance, Over Stowey, Somerset
National Farmers' Union	South West Region, Exeter
Mrs M Roberts	Plympton
Mr R Baker	Umberleigh
Mr C Foreman	Carlton TV
Mr J Worth	SW Region, Countryside Agency, Exeter
Devon County Council	Mr A Smith, Director of Education, Arts and Libraries, Exeter
Elm Farm Research Centre	
Mr G Bateman	Environment Agency (Devon Area), Exeter
Western Morning News	Plymouth
Farm Crisis Network (South West)	
Mr G Gilbert	Great Western Radio
Mr T Griffith-Jones	Wellington, Somerset
Mr G Willis	Plympton
Devon and Cornwall Constabulary Exeter	
Ms D Pring	Federation of Small Businesses (Devon Regional Office), Torquay
Mr E Braxton Reynolds	Tickle and Reynolds, Public Analyst's Laboratory, Exeter
Mr P Penning	Bratton Clovelly Parish Council

Mr A Milward	Drewsteignton Parish Council
Mr G Adams	Morebath Parish Council
Mrs B Down	Ashford Parish Council
Mr H Sampson	Ashford
Ms M Costa	Totnes
Mr P Snell	Sandford
Mr J Hillson	Bere Alston
Mr W Reed	Templeton
Mrs P Woods	Family Farmers' Association, Kingsbridge
Taste of the West	Exeter
Ms A Thomas	Great Torrington
Mr V Carden	Maldon, Essex
Mr M Banks	Petrockstowe
Mr A Boyt	Davidstow, Cornwall
Mr J Bhakta	Sidbury
Mr H Wilkinson	
Mrs C Harding	Farway
Mr D Sibley	Witheridge
Mr D Sykes & Mr D Stephens	Inwardleigh
Mrs L Elt	Exeter
Mr C Dwyer	Lynton/Lynmouth Town Council
Mrs S Vergette	Highampton
Mr T Price	Exeter
Mr W Banting	Muddiford
Ms M Kramer	DEFRA, Exeter
Mr S Machin	Western Counties Agricultural Valuers, Exeter
Mr C Caffin	Tiverton
P Gordon	Tiverton
Mr J Talbot	Community Council of Devon, Exeter
Mr P Turner	Chawleigh
Mr B Inwood	Christow
Mr D Pitches	Jennycliff Holidays, Plymouth
Ms V Lay	Brayford
Mr A Davies	Horwood
Ms J Richardson	Exmouth
Mrs S Robinson	Teignmouth
Mr B Jones	Eastleigh

Mrs B Ewing	The Duchy School, Bradninch
Ms R Lane	Tavistock
Bridestowe Primary School	
Ms C Borgen	Exeter
Mr P Clarke and Ms S Sparrow	Plymouth
Ms J Young	Plymouth
Ms G Quiggin	Woodlands Park Primary School, Ivybridge
Mr & Mrs J Sims	Dulverton, Somerset
H Tozer	Stoke Hill First School, Exeter
Mr P Burgess	Chudleigh
Mr R Wills	Ilsington
Ms N Sinclair	South Brent
Ms S Downs	Budleigh Salterton
Ms S Levy	North Devon Arts, Barnstaple
Clawton Primary School	
Clinton School	Merton
Ms M Barker	Totnes
H Pirwany	
Dr T Hughes-Davies	Fordingbridge, Hampshire
B Clapham	Christow
Mr A Barnes	Morebath
S Higdon	Cornwood Primary School
Mr P Collins	Merton
Mr G Bond	Langtree
Mr M Badcock	Kings Nympton Parish Council
North Bovey Parish Council	
Mr R Croslegh	Horns Cross
Mr M Beeson	Manaton
Mr S Heath	Chittlehampton
Ms L Ferrand	Topsham
Ms M Govier	Crediton
Mr C Lott	Spreyton
Ms M Tucker	Okehampton
Ms C Smith	Chudleigh Parish Council
Ms R Day	Kingsteignton
Devon County Council	Mr T Jones, Devon Youth Music, Exeter
North Devon Marketing Bureau Barnstaple	

Dr S Barnes	Hockworthy
Mrs M Williamson	Meavy Church of England Primary School
L Lewin	South Devon Herd Book Society, Bradworthy and Clyst St Mary
Ms M Bishop	Rattery
Mrs H Wills	Denbury and Torbryan Parish Council
Mr J Phelps	Exeter
Mr A Westaway	Chulmleigh
Mr A Murdin	Devon Guild of Craftsmen, Bovey Tracey
Protect our Wild Animals	Exeter
J Budden	Burrington
Ms J Pearce	Chittlehamholt
Mrs D Irwin	Kingsteignton
Mr J Irwin	Kingsteignton
Mr R Irwin	Kings Nympton
Mr M Rolls	Princetown
Mrs P Bown	Wembworthy
Mr M Jones	Bideford
Ms C and Mr R Thomas	Muddiford
Mr M Gibson	Exmouth
Ilfracombe and District Tourism Association	
Mr A Clements	South Tawton
Ms G and Mr W Douglas-Mann Petrockstowe	
Stokenham Parish Council	
Mr A Giddings	North Devon Theatres, Barnstaple
Tavistock Town Council	
Mr C Hodgson	Diocese of Exeter, Agricultural/Rural Ministry Support Group, Parracombe
Mr D and Mr E Williams	Bickington
Ms J Parsons	Holne
Mr L and Ms K Wright	Ilfracombe
Mr P Kent	Hatherleigh
Miss S Coffin	South Molton
Devon County Council	Mr P Berry, Outdooor and Residential Education Service, Exeter

Silence at Ramscliffe

The photographs on the following pages chronicle the experience of a Devon farm as the shadow of the Foot and Mouth epidemic fell upon it in 2001. These photographs are not intended to be representative of the wide range of different circumstances that so many Devon farming families had to endure during that year. Instead they stand as a singular and – despite their harsh reality – an elegiac testimony of how life changed on this one farm as the Devon countryside fell silent in the Spring of 2001.

For those whose lives were not directly affected by Foot and Mouth in 2001, the memories of the epidemic's impact may have already begun to fade. These photographs capture the sad picture of slaughter, of pain and of descending and consuming silence that so many farms experienced during the epidemic. They start with the everyday scene of cows being milked in the milking parlour; they finish with that same milking parlour left redundant and spotlessly clean - and a sheepdog in an empty farmyard with no animals to tend and nothing to do.

The value of these images stems directly from the alert and sympathetic eye of their creator, the noted Devon photographer, Chris Chapman. For over 25 years, Chris Chapman has been living among and working with farming families in Devon. Over this period, he has created a unique record of rural lives and landscapes. At the outbreak of the Foot and Mouth epidemic, it seemed only natural to look to him to create this sad, but essential record of the realities experienced on one Devon farm.

Philip Lake milking his cows before their contiguous cull

Vet sealing the lane to the farm on the morning of the cull

Philip Lake herding the cattle down into the farmyard prior to their slaughter

MAFF employee moving cattle prior to their slaughter

Philip Lake taking bedding down to the silage clamp prior to slaughter

MAFF employees spreading straw in the silage clamp prior to slaughter

Sedating the store cattle prior to their slaughter

Stunning a dairy cow

MAFF employee monitoring the sedation of the dairy herd in the silage clamp

Slaughtered cows

The slaughtered dairy herd lying in the silage clamp

Vet with the calves prior to their sedation

MAFF employees sedating the calves prior to slaughter

Moving the calves to slaughter

Carrying the last calf to slaughter

Preparing the pyre to burn the slaughtered cattle

The smouldering pyre after the burn

Percy Lake and Mitchell Bright cleaning the cubicles after the slaughter

Redundant milking parlour after it had been cleaned and disinfected

The empty silage clamp after it had been cleaned and disinfected

Empty fields and smoking pyres - the aftermath of Foot and Mouth on a Devon farm

A dog with nothing to do: Ben in the empty farmyard after the slaughter

Chris Chapman was commissioned to take these photographs by Beaford Arts with the support of Devon County Council. For over 30 years Beaford Arts, as a pioneering rural charity, has been enriching, through the arts, the lives of communities and individuals across the scattered landscapes of north Devon. The Beaford Photographic Archive (in which a larger selection of these photographs is being deposited) today stands as a rural record of regional and national importance, reaching back to the nineteenth century and looking forward into the twenty first.

Chris Chapman's photographs are published here for the first time thanks to the co-operation of Beaford Arts (Director, Jennie Hayes), Philip and Percy Lake, and Robert Kilby.